Rosie Wells Enterprises, Inc.

Secondary Market Price Guide
to

(BOYDS BEARS & FRIENDS)™

Includes Bearstones,™ Folkstones,™ Dollstones™
and Shoe Box Bears™

Editor and Collector
Rosalie "Rosie" J. Wells

Published by Rosie Wells Enterprises, Inc.
22341 E. Wells Rd., Canton, IL 61520
Phone: 309/668-2211 Fax: 309/668-2795

Visit us on the Internet!
🐾 http://www.RosieWells.com 🐾
E-Mail address: Rosie@RosieWells.com

Rosalie 'Rosie' Wells

'Author, Editor, Collector, Wife, Mother, Grandma'

In researching the prices of these fabulous li'l figurines, we found the 1Es are the most sought after. (First Edition – From the first molds – approximately 3,600) The 2Es are almost as popular, as they are the next 3,600 numbered pieces to be produced. Due to the 6,000 plus retailers wanting more 1Es, we will probably see another 1,200 1Es added to the production numbers of the Bearstones® in 1997, bringing the total to 4,800 figurines per 1E. This would still be considered a "low" production when a col-

lectible is as hot as the Bearstones. Fewer avid collectors collect the Dollstones™ and Folkstones®, but they are quite popular. They have their own look and are a pleasant addition to the Boyds Collection™! I have all the Dollstones and my favorite Folkstones, as well as many of the Bearstones! I love to search for the very scarce ones, don't you?! Finding one is like a garage sale "find" that is the big talk at the beauty salon for months! Ha!

To date, after 3Es, current pieces' secondary market values have not escalated. Not until they receive the knighted touch of retirement do we find that "any edition number" will satisfy if 1Es aren't on the retailer's shelf!

Different paint colors often excite the avid collector to seek out the change. Keep your eyes open for GCC and NALED exclusive figurines (Gift Creations Concepts catalog exclusives and National Association of Limited Edition Dealers). These figurines sometimes have different colors on them.

One good example of a color change is *ms. griz*. The first 1E through 6Es were pink. The "Head Bean" wanted blue, so her

attire was changed to blue. The 1E pink is the nicest one to find. If you don't care about edition numbers, any pink will thrill you! Should *ms. griz* continue for two or more years, any pink edition will definitely be a fun one to own.

I have met the "Head Bean Hisself" and have talked with his wife, Tina, many times. What a fun couple. They are producing very special collectibles for all of us. They also produce plush bears and animals. Maybe those will be published in another guide down the road! These are Hot, Hot, too!

Not only are Boyds collectibles at selected retailers, but one may purchase them exclusively on QVC from time to time (a home shopping channel). These are marked as a "Premiere Edition." To date, Dollstones have taken the lead with this type of debut. They have sparked collector enthusiasm and caused more involvement, in my opinion, in all phases of the Boyds Collection. Gary's personal debuts on TV certainly gained him a large following!

Write to me and send photos of you and your displays. I'd like to share them with other collectors. We're all one big family. You may want to subscribe to the *Weekly Collectors' Gazette*™ to keep updated every week on hot tips for Boyds Bears collectors. For lots of collector news and photos, subscribe to the bimonthly *Collectors' Bulletin*™! If you're a bear collector, you won't be able to put this magazine down until you've read it all! Other collectibles are covered also. Just call my office for information. Enjoy this guide. We hope it adds to your pleasure of collecting the fastest growing collectible in the USA!

Rosie

Gary M. Lowenthal

"The Head Bean Hisself"

G.M. Lowenthal … Chief Designer, President and "Head Bean Hisself" of The Boyds Collection, Ltd., was born in New York City in 1949. After graduating from Alfred University in Upstate New York, he spent time touring the world with the U.S. Peace Corps. Upon his return to New York, he was employed by Bloomingdale's for seven years, learning the ins and outs of purchasing, design and merchandising. With all this exposure to the great designers of the world, Gary took his big bold step and moved to Boyds, Maryland, to start *The Boyds Collection, Ltd.* (Ta Da!), an out-of-the-way antique shop in rural Maryland.

Gary's first attempt at success was, of course, to start a line of very fine hand-carved wooden Duck Decoys. Along with that, he also decided to design miniature ceramic houses called *The Gnomes' Homes.*

In 1987, Gary moved his business, his growing family and "hisself" to historic Gettysburg, PA. It is there where Gary's claim to fame can be established as he, along with a notable teddy bear designer, Gae Sharp, began designing a line of collectible plush Teddy Bears, Hares, Tabbies, Pooches, etc. This line of plush now encompasses over 300 different styles from 3" miniatures to 21" giants. Many are award winners or nominees, and each year limited editions are issued.

In 1992, Gary began designing cold cast sculptural interpretations of his now famous Bears, Tabbies, Moose, etc., adding to the growing line of Boyds Collectibles. The line can extend as far as Lowenthal's imagination. He says he doesn't know how or from where or when the next good idea will come. *"One of the things I think people enjoy the most about the Bearstones is their off-center sense of humor, as well as the extraordinary detail and surprises that you find if you look carefully."* He adds, *"I think that there's a surprise for everyone with each Bearstone."*

Acknowledgements

Rosie Wells Enterprises, Inc., wishes to thank all who helped in any way to compile the data in this premiere edition guide.

Thanks again to our friends Pat Santos, Janet Hymes and Janet Bryan for their research contributions.

A special thanks to Nina Long who has done hours of research and to Jennifer Brush for her typing skills, Michelle Ford and Julie Wells for art design and others on my staff who also made it all happen.

Thanks to the Boyds staff who have so graciously helped us with so many questions and the use of their photography and logos. Great collection folks! Keep creating, Gary!

III

Beary Interesting

The Boyds Collection, Ltd., is taking the collectible world on a whirl! Being first with the rough texture design of the bears' fur to the delicate lace of Emily, the Dollstone™ we will be sure to enjoy these collections for years to come.

The markings of edition sizes, low production numbers and the limited editions have satisfied the avid collector who makes the "collectible scene" happen. The 1Es are very, very scarce on retailers' shelves and some may be disappointed at times due to the scarcity, but scarcity has been a big part of all the enthusiasm for these quality produced collectibles.

This guide has been researched to add to your enthusiasm of collecting Boyds Bears and Friends™. We'll be the first to say there may be an error or two, but we really, really worked 'til the wee hours of the night to give you the best guide for The Boyds Collection. We have examined nearly every piece in all the collections with the help of collectors, retailers and the Boyds Company! We hope enjoy the fruits of our labor! Please feel free to share your insight and expertise with us.

Send or call with your ideas, additions and photos for next year's guide. Send to: Rosie Wells Enterprises, Inc. Attention: BB Guide Research Dept. 22341 E. Wells Rd. Canton, IL 61520

Enjoy your collection for the love of it… I love every piece! I enjoy the Dollstones and have them all. The Bears are so special, too! Folkstones make me laugh… just enjoy every piece!

To capitalize or not to capitalize was our question to each other when deciding the format of each little character's name to be printed in this guide. We found most of the Boyds' brochures had small letters beginning the names, but capital letters were used on several of the actual pieces. (*bailey* #2000 did not even have her name on her base.) So, when studying your pieces, be aware we know of this and really do not consider it significant when evaluating their secondary market value.

The Boyds Collection, Ltd., began creating Antique Reproductions and Collectibles in 1979. It was not until 1993 that the first Bearstone was introduced to collectors. Ta da! Wow – Instant success!

Although Boyds' Bearwear and Folkwear pins are a fun collectible, we have chosen not to list them in our guide because there are so many and we have not seen secondary market sales on these to date. Five **Bearwear pins** will be retiring as of December, 1997. They are: *daphne with dove* (#2611), *amelia* (#2612), *bailey's springtime* (#2617), *justina, bailey & m. harrison* (#2619) and *angelica's flight* (#2605). Six **Folkwear pins** will be retiring as of December, 1997. They are: *alice & emily* (#2666), *daphne in straw hat* (#2668), *florence wingsit* (#2625), *ariel...the guardian* (#2671), *oceania* (#2674) and *ralph...angel pooch* (#2669).

🐾 We never know the actual amount of editions produced, but we do know that the size of each edition is limited to a certain number of pieces before the edition number is changed. When the edition number changes, the piece number reverts to "0001" For example, after 1E/3600 the next figurine would be marked 2E/0001. To date, there is no proof from any research as to how many editions were produced for each piece.

🐾 The edition and individual registration is stamped on the underside of the base just above the style number:

(**Boyds Bears & Friends™**

THE BEARSTONE COLLECTION ®

"I always remember an epitaph . . . 'Here lies Jake Williams. He done his damnedest.' I think that is the greatest epitaph a man can have - when he gives everything that is in him to do the job he has before him."
- Harry S Truman

Edition / pc #   **SE/1089**

STYLE #2279 Sir Edmund . . . Persistence

EDITION SIZES FOR THE BOYDS COLLECTION TO DATE (late '96-early '97):

✳ Folkstones, Santa & Friends, Bearstones, Folkstones and Santa & Friends Waterglobes, Bearstone Votives, and edition numbered Bear Ornaments have been produced in edition sizes of thirty six hundred pieces (3,600 1Es; 3,600 2Es; etc.). It's my opinion we may see more 1Es in the near future,

perhaps from 3,600 to 4,800. Hopefully, if this proves too many, then a change back to a smaller edition size will be reconsidered.

✳ DOLLSTONES, Dollstone Waterglobes and FOLKSTONE FAIRIES, to date, have been produced in edition sizes of 4,800.

✳ SHOE BOX BEARS have been produced in edition sizes of 6,000.

✳ The CHRISTMAS PAGEANT appears in edition sizes of 7,200. The final production of the entire Christmas Pageant Bearstones will be December 31, 1999, at which time the molds will be destroyed and this part of the Boyds Bearstone Collection will never be produced again. To date, there is evidence that the production quantity (7,200) on these pieces has not brought about enthusiasm for the secondary market as the lower production editions of 3,600. Not everything produced has to be scarce, though...

🐾 First editions (1Es) are sought after by the avid collectors. The 2Es, 3Es and 4Es are becoming editions which satisfy many collectors due to the scarcity of 1Es. We're seeing this in our research and recording known averaged sales for this premiere edition. (To date, there are approximately 6,150 retailers and there are only 3,600 1Es.) The Boyds company cannot supply every retailer with even one 1E.

🐾 Gary Lowenthal has signed many figurines for collectors at Expos and store signings. I would suggest that you insure a signed figurine for $10-$15 over secondary market value or, if a new figurine, over retail. A piece should be signed for sentimental reasons, to remember when you met the artist, not "gotta get it signed for my profit!"

🐾
v

🐾 An understamp found on many Boyds pieces including Folkstones, Dollstones and Bearstones is the GCC understamp. GCC stands for Gift Creations Concepts, a catalog syndicate program. Retailers who join GCC offer several companies' products.

```
Edition / pc # 2E/1399
Certified By: J.M. ✏️ ❗
STYLE #3512-01GCC Courtney w/ Phoebe .
Over the River and Through the Woods
©1996 O THE BOYDS COLLECTION LTD
HANDMADE IN CHINA
```

These syndicated offerings may be the only pieces from a company's line that many dealers can offer. For example, some have not received a dealership from Boyds, etc., but they are a member of a catalog syndicate. These figurines usually are early releases and sometimes have different coloring than the figurine that will be distributed in the regular line.

🐾 NALED, National Association of Limited Edition Dealers, is a retail trade association. The Shoe Box Bear, *gladys,* is a NALED catalog exclusive from The Boyds Collection. All *gladys* figurines will be understamped 1E. (See page 38.)

🐾 Because of the popularity of purchasing first editions, it has come to our attention that there are those individuals who alter edition numbers by using a solution on a "Q-tip" and remove one of the two digit edition numbers. For example, changing an 11E to a 1E. So be careful when purchasing hard-to-find 1E pieces.

🐾 Be aware of fakes! When ya got a good thing – others will copy! Of course, a plain unmarked base is possible; it has happened with other collectibles, but it's rare. When shopping for The Boyds Collection, always look for the symbol of authenticity found on every figurine.

🐾 On Bearstones you will find a bear paw 🐾 , Folkstones have a star ⭐ , a shoe imprint is on the Dollstones 👣 , and on Santa Bears, there is a tree imprint 🌲 . It's fun to discover where these are hidden.

🐾 A version of the very first *bailey with suitcase* with no edition number was produced for a 90 day period. She came with a very large pink bow on her head. (The texture on the very first design was not soooo good!)

🐾 Also produced during this 90 day period was *father chrisbear* (#2008) without a base. These were pictured in a Boyds 1993 brochure and have been verified by Boyds. Should you have either *father chrisbear* without a base or *bailey* with a very large pink bow on her head, we would love to hear from you. We do not have good color photos of these pieces. A secondary market value has not been established because sales have not been found at the time of this printing but they are scarce. If I had one, I'd insure it for at least $500... maybe more. Your input is welcomed.

BEARSTONES™

🐾 A Boyds' Homecoming Weekend was held on July 27, 1996, at Koony's Barn in Littleton, Pennsylvania. Gary informally introduced his Shoe Box Bears at that time. There were approximately thirty sets (all 1Es) which quickly sold out!

🐾 Only 3,600 1Es of the *clarion* bear (#2254CL) were issued through the Clarion, Iowa, Chamber of Commerce in 1995. She is the same as *bailey sweetie pie* (#2254) except the Clarion *bailey* is wearing a pink bow and is holding a round pie with "Clarion ♥ Iowa" printed on it. (See page 21.)

🐾 To date, five Bearstones have been produced for **CANADA.** They are *lefty on the mound* (#BC2056), *homer on the plate* (#2218), *elf bear with list* (#2252), *big pig/little pig* (#2256) and *ewell & walton* (#2228CN). You'll find those Canadian stores advertising in *The Collectors Bulletin*™ in the *"Just the Bear Facts"* section. We've heard very low edition numbers are being found on limited edition Boyds figurines in Canada.

🐾 *ms. griz... monday morning* (#2276) has been found with a color variation. When she was first released she wore a pink dress with a blue bow and she sat on a bluish gray chair. She is the favorite to look for. *ms. griz* has now been changed as she appears in the catalog. She wears a blue dress with a red bow. A red bow is also on her head and she sits in a tan leather-looking chair.

🐾 For me finding such errors is next to the feeling I had as a child finding my little blond Cocker Spaniel in my Christmas stocking on Christmas morning! Wow! My biggest thrill was finding a pink *ms. griz* (see page 26) and *etheral* (see page 53) at the same store on the same day! I nearly walked right out the door without opening it! I'm lucky I got home safely! When I find something such as this, it makes me want to pack my suitcase and get on the road to search for more!

🐾 The Shoe Box Bears™ represent the Head Bean and his parents when he was a small tyke. Also, in the collection are a miniature bench, chairs and tiny handmade quilts which create a setting for the bears. These bears are packaged in small shoe boxes which were almost as difficult to create as the jointed resin bears. The boxes have a handmade look, with artwork on the sides and top. Even specially printed tissue paper was designed to package the bears! The first Shoe Box Bears debuted on QVC (A 24 hour shop at home television show) and were marked Q96. Later editions were marked 1E, 2E, 3E, etc. There are 6,000 in each edition of these Shoe Box Bears. Because of the difficulty in marking the inner leg, a certificate with the edition and piece number was to be enclosed in the box by late 1996. It is not clear how many editions were produced before they began placing certificates in the box.

FOLKSTONES™

🐾 "GRS Edition" literally means General ReSculpt or ReSculpt. It is a new version of an already introduced older figurine. As with any new molds, the edition numbers start with 1E. *To date, only Folkstones and Santa & Friends have been found with GRS Editions.* The words "GRS Edition" or "RS Edition" will be found on the understamp of the figurine (below).

🐾 Pictured below is *angel of love* (#2821). This figurine was introduced in a GRS Edition which is pictured on the right. It has a few differences from its original version; the texture is smooth and the eyes on both the angel and child are somewhat different than the original. There are no formal retirements for original molds, but this particular figurine (#2821) both the original and the "GRS Edition" retired December, 1996. These "GRS Editions" are meant to be an improvement of an already great figurine. I often wonder if the original molds just gave out and new pieces had to be resculpted.

🐾 Poochstones™ debuted in February of 1996. They are a part of the Folkstone Collection. These are popular but we have not received as much feedback from collectors and retailers regarding this collection as compared with the others. I have several!

🐾 *betty cocker*, one of the Boyds Folkstones, no longer carries this name.

On new pieces, her name was changed to *betty biscuit,* as the original name was too similar to "Betty Crocker." Look for *betty cocker!* It's fun to look for changes!

🐾 The first truly numbered Limited Edition Folkstone was *nanick & siegfried von hindenmoose with elliot* (#2807), also known as *"the plan."* (See page 49.) This triple figure sculpture is understamped and numbered 1 through 10,000. When the 10,000th piece is produced, the molds will be broken and the piece retired. Canadian pieces were stamped with a C before the handwritten number.

DOLLSTONES™

🐾 Yesterday's Child™... The Dollstone Collection™ debuted in August of 1995 on QVC, the "shop on tv" show. The Dollstones introduced and sold on QVC were *victoria with samantha* (#3502), *betsy with edmund* (#3503), *megan with elliot & annie* (#3504) and *katherine with amanda and edmund* (#3505). Premier Issue first editions were sold only on QVC. These style numbers (#3502-3505) were then produced for retailers. The first four are the most sought after due to the 3,600 production amount. The others are not as hard to locate. We've learned a retail chain (Kirlin's) will have a Limited Edition (3,600) Dollstone, *jean with elliot and debbie... the bakers* (#3510) in a different color in late '96 or early '97.

🐾 "Premier Edition" was reported on *jennifer with priscilla* (#3500) and *patricia with molly"* (#3501) yet these two Dollstones never appeared on QVC.

🐾 Pictured is an example of a "Premier Edition" understamp. The first "Premier Edition" Dollstones were limited to 3,600 pieces. Because these were the "first" and were unknown, many of today's avid collectors did not acquire them from QVC. They have had to seek them out on the secondary market. These first four designs of 3,600 were instant money makers for those who bought the limit of five per person from QVC.

BOYDS COLLECTION

THE DOLLSTONE COLLECTION ™

"What is a Friend? A single soul dwelling in two bodies."
- Aristotle

Premier Edition / #   1 E/285

Certified By: *M S.*

G M Lowenthal
The Head Bean Hisself

STYLE #3502 Victoria with Samantha
©1995 THE BOYDS COLLECTION LTD

🐾 Up through October, 1996, three QVC shows featured Premier Edition Dollstones™. Set one consisted of *victoria with samantha* (#3502), *betsy with edmund* (#3503), *megan with elliot and annie* (#3504) and *katherine with amanda and edmund* (#3505). Set two consisted of *ashley* (#3506), *tea party* (#3507), *emily* (#3508) and *rebecca* (#3509). Set three consisted of *jean with elliot and debbie* (#3510), *michelle with daisy* (#3511), *candice with matthew gathering apples* (#3514) and *mallory with patsy and jb* (#3517). Each Premier Edition was offered separately. Set one has been the most sought after due to the fact that it was the introduction of a new product and many of today's present Dollstones collectors were not alerted to this debut of only 3,600, nor were they even collec-

tors of Dollstones. The other Dollstones debuted at 4,800 per edition. (Read Rosie's *Weekly Collectors' Gazette™* for advance notice of such events on QVC, etc.)

🐾 To Buy, Sell or Trade your Boyds Collectibles, call 1-900-740-7575, Press 48. $2.00 per minute, use a touch tone phone. You must be 18 years old.
To hear Rosie's Weekly Hot Tips on The Boyds Collection' press the * (the star) key! Located below the # 7 on the key pad.

🐾 Collectors and retailers advertise in *The Collectors Bulletin™* and the *Weekly Collectors' Gazette™.* You'll locate retailers in Canada there also! Send $2.00 for a sample of the *Weekly*; you won't be able to stop with just one issue! Call us for information on how to order the *Collectors Bulletin™* and the *Weekly Collectors' Gazette™* 1-800-445-8745.

🐾 Thank your Boyds' dealer for offering this guide. Be loyal to them and they'll remember you when those 1Es and Limited Editions arrive at their shops!

🐾 While on vacation, we encourage you to take your guide along to show other retailers. For some un"bear"able reason, they may not know it exists. Oh me, Oh my! Thanks for purchasing this guide! We hope you'll be even more excited over these li'l characters and you'll go shopping the first chance you get for more, more Boyds pieces!! Happy Collecting!

Rosie

Errors

Errors are very rare in the Boyds Collection. At this time we can only report two which we can also verify with photos.

The photo on the top left was sent to us from Sharon R. of Minnesota. Her photo clearly shows the telephone facing the opposite direction as the current design, what we're seeing on today's current piece. The photo at right shows the correct version of the figurine.

Bottom left is an errored figurine found by Susan H. of Minnesota. Her photo has the words "RUE LOVE" above *grenville and beatrice* (#2274). The picture bottom right was taken from a 1996 Boyds Collector's Catalog, however, we have learned that the photo is a prototype. (A prototype is a figurine presented for final approval before production.) Notice the birds on the top left side of the trellis on the photo at right.

Incorrect versions   Correct versions

Table of Contents

Rosie & The Head Bean Hisself

How to Use This Guide

The entire Boyds collection is listed in numerical order by their item number.

① 2003-04 ② grenville ③ □
④ with green scarf
⑤ "... take good Care of yourself, you belong to me..."
⑥ **RETIRED DECEMBER, 1993**
⑦ COMMENTS: Issued June 1993, *Orig. S.R.* $11.00
🐾 Only produced in two editions before retirement. He is becoming scarce and highly sought after. With only 7,200 pieces produced, this is truly an exlusive bear. The numeral 2003 was imprinted on the understamp.
⑧ 1E $375–$425   2E $375–$425
⑨ Have _____ Want _____ Price Paid _____

---

1   Style/order number

2   Figurine's name or names

3   Instant Alert – Do I or do I not have this piece. If this piece is a part of your collection, mark ✓ in the box.

4   The inspiration is located on the underside of the base.

5   Many of the Boyds figurines have a quote or saying on the base that relates to that certain piece. Some of the quotes are from famous people and others are created by the "Head Bean Hisself!"

6   If retired before press time, you'll be told in bold letters!

7   Comments: Contains year of introduction, editor's comments, differences, errors, etc. Each year's guide may contain added information, reporting variations, changes and new information from collectors, etc.

8   The secondary market values are affected by the edition numbers. Usually, the lower the edition number, the greater the secondary market value of the piece unless an error has been found. If the word "up" is listed after the edition number (ex. **4E up**), then all productions from 4E on up will have same value. If the word "up" comes after a value then the prices could possibly go up even after press time. Use these prices as a "guide" to resell, buy or insure your collection. Always do your own research as prices may fluctuate from time to time!

9   Check these boxes to record the price you paid and if you have or want this piece. Great for others to peek at for special gift giving!

Every effort has been made to assure this guide is complete and accurate. Use the prices in this guide only as a guide to help determine the value of your pieces for insurance evaluation.

XII

BEARSTONES™

2000   bailey bear   ☐
with suitcase (smooth texture)
"... a journey... begins with a single step."
RETIRED DECEMBER, 1993

COMMENTS: Issued September 1993, *Orig. S.R.* $14.50
🐾 This piece is fun to search for. It has a very smooth texture and a brown base. All pieces were marked 1E and there were approximately 10,000 released. There was another variation of this bear in which *bailey* had a very large pink bow. A copy of a Boyds brochure has been seen with this *bailey* with a very large pink bow. We have been told this bear, with the very large bow, was produced for 90 days. To date, no secondary market sales have been found for this bear with a very large bow.

1E $85-90

Have _____ Want _____ Price Paid _____

2000   bailey bear   ☐
with suitcase (today's "rough" texture)
"... a journey... begins with a single step."

COMMENTS: Issued October 1993, *Orig. S.R.* $14.50
🐾 This is a very popular piece with lots of detail. The suitcase has socks hanging out of it due to the hurried packing. This bear has rough textured fur and a white base. Very rare bear in early editions!

1E $420   **2E $230**   **3E $150**
4E up $14.50

Have _____ Want _____ Price Paid _____

2001   simone de bearvoire & her mom   ☐
"... a mother's love."
RETIRED SEPTEMBER, 1993

COMMENTS: Issued June 1993, *Orig. S.R.* $14.50
🐾 Unsure how many editions were produced. The book was much larger and the entire piece was much smoother when it first debuted. In the later editions (see next entry) *simone & her mom* have patches on their feet. Was not as popular then as others that debuted with her.

1E $280   **2E $200**   **3E $180**
4E up $125

Have _____ Want _____ Price Paid _____

2001   **simone de bearvoire & her mom**   ☐
"... a mother's love."
RETIRED DECEMBER, 1996
COMMENTS: Issued September 1993, *Orig. S.R.* $14.50
🐾 This piece makes an excellent Mother's Day or baby shower gift. It is more detailed than the first editions with patches being added to the molds for the paws. This change started somewhere in the 5th edition.

5E $80	6E $50	7E up $30

Have _____Want_____Price Paid _____

2002   **neville**   ☐
the bedtime bear
"... And so Fall asleep, Love, Loved by Thee..."
RETIRED DECEMBER, 1996
COMMENTS: Issued June 1993, *Orig. S.R.* $14.50
🐾 All of your dreams will be filled with love when *neville* the bedtime bear is around. Z-z-z-z

1E $95-$100	2E $75	3E $65-70

4E up $50
Have _____Want_____Price Paid _____

2003   **arthur**   ☐
with red scarf
"... take good Care of yourself, you belong to me..."
RETIRED DECEMBER, 1994
COMMENTS: Issued June 1993, *Orig. S.R.* $11.00
🐾 Although hardly noticeable, slight differences in coloring and size set *arthur* apart from the rest of his buddies in this collection.

1E $105-115	2E $90	3E $75

4E up $60
Have _____Want_____Price Paid _____

2003-03   arthur   ☐
with red scarf
"... take good Care of yourself, you belong to me..."
RETIRED DECEMBER, 1994
COMMENTS: Issued June 1993, *Orig. S.R.* $11.00
🐾 The lighter color of *arthur* sets him apart from all the others.
1E $140-$150   2E $90   3E $60
4E up $35
Have _____ Want_____Price Paid _____

2003-04   grenville   ☐
with green scarf
"... take good Care of yourself, you belong to me..."
RETIRED DECEMBER, 1993
COMMENTS: Issued June 1993, *Orig. S.R.* $11.00
🐾 Scarce! Only produced in two editions before retirement. He is becoming scarce and highly sought after. With only 7,200 pieces produced, this is truly an elusive bear. The numeral 2003 was imprinted on the understamp.
1E $375-$425   2E $375-$425
Have _____ Want_____Price Paid _____

2003-08   grenville   ☐
with red scarf
"... take good Care of yourself, you belong to me..."
RETIRED DECEMBER, 1995
COMMENTS: Issued June 1993, *Orig. S.R.* $11.00
🐾 This edition of *grenville* is just as popular as all the other *grenville* pieces. The numeral 2003 was imprinted on the understamp.
1E $140-$150   2E $75-80   3E $70
4E up $65
Have _____ Want_____Price Paid _____

2004   **victoria**
the lady
"Love is, above all the gift of oneself."
– Anouilh

COMMENTS: Issued June 1993, *Orig. S.R.* $18.50

🐾 A very cute piece with Victorian flair. Her hat box turns into a trinket box! The bear paw can be found on the piece and inside the hat box. This is the first box figurine produced.

1E $225   **2E $175**   **3E $150**
4E up $18.50

Have _____ Want_____ Price Paid _____

2005   **moriarity**
the bear in the cat suit
"... boo!"
RETIRED DECEMBER, 1995

COMMENTS: Issued June 1993, *Orig. S.R.* $14.00

🐾 From the first edition (1E) through the eleventh edition (11E) the copyright is found on the side of the base. Somewhere in the eleventh edition, a change was made and the copyright is found on the top of the base. Hood and cuffs are larger and the head is tilted.

1E $120   **2E $85**   **3E $70**
4E up $65

Have _____ Want_____ Price Paid _____

2006   **bailey**
in the orchard
"... Life's Harvest."
RETIRED DECEMBER, 1996

COMMENTS: Issued June 1993, *Orig. S.R.* $14.50

🐾 A delightfully detailed piece.

1E $225   **2E $120**   **3E $115**
4E up $65

Have _____ Want_____ Price Paid _____

2007   **wilson**   ☐
with love sonnets
"... how do I Love Thee..."
– Elizabeth Barrett Browning
TO BE RETIRED DECEMBER, 1997
COMMENTS: Issued June 1993, *Orig. S.R.* $13.00
🐾 To date, up to 24 editions have been reported.
Many were sold as Valentine presents.

1E $500-$550   **2E $375**   **3E $200**
4E up $13

Have _____ Want_____ Price Paid _____

2008   **father chrisbear & son**   ☐
"... Have a Beary Merry Christmas."
RETIRED DECEMBER, 1993
COMMENTS: Issued June 1993, *Orig. S.R.* $15.00
🐾 A Boyds 1993 brochure pictures this piece without
a base; it was produced for 90 days. No secondary
market sales have been seen, to date, for this bear
with no base. The *father chrisbear and son* pictured is
the piece most collectors own. It is not clear how
many were produced. One report we have is that there
were around 10,000 pieces produced. Another report
stated that there were only 3,600 pieces produced.

1E $350

Have _____ Want_____ Price Paid _____

2010   **byron & chedda**   ☐
with catmint
*"... one is closer to God in a Garden than
in anyplace else on Earth..."*
RETIRED, 1994
COMMENTS: Issued June 1993, *Orig. S.R.* $14.20
🐾 There were no patches on the left arm in the 1Es
through part of the 3Es. Somewhere in the third edition, a patch was added to the left arm (mold change).

1E $120   **2E $95**
3E – no patch $75   **3E – with patch $80**
4E up $55

Have _____ Want_____ Price Paid _____

2011   **daphne hare & maisey ewe** ☐

"... sometimes I've believed as many as six impossible things before breakfast."
– Lewis Carroll
RETIRED DECEMBER, 1995
COMMENTS: Issued June 1993, *Orig. S.R.* $14.50
🐾 First "hare" produced, very special piece. Extremely hard to find.

1E $130   **2E $80**   **3E $55**
4E up $14.50
Have _____Want_____Price Paid _____

2012   **christian**
by the sea

"... there is nothing, absolutely nothing, half so much worth doing as simply messing about... with boats."
– Wind in the Willows
COMMENTS: Issued June 1993, *Orig. S.R.* $14.50
🐾 This piece is very popular along coastal Maine. The name depicts the serenity of this piece. He really looks like a piece that would be honored with retirement.

1E $110   **2E $70**   **3E $50**
4E up $14.50
Have _____Want_____Price Paid _____

2014   **bailey's birthday** ☐

"We are always the same age inside..."
COMMENTS: Issued January 1994, *Orig S.R.* $16.00
🐾 How true this inscription is! All *bailey* pieces are great, but this one takes the cake.

1E $185   **2E $130**   **3E $95**
4E up $16
Have _____Want_____Price Paid _____

2015   **justina & m. harrison**
           sweetie pie

"Whatever you do, put romance &
enthusiasm into the life of our children."
– Margaret Ramsay MacDonald

COMMENTS: Issued January 1994, *Orig. S.R.* $26.00
🐾 Warms the heart of all. Great to display on a
kitchen shelf!

1E $95   **2E $45**   **3E $35**
4E up $26

Have _____ Want_____ Price Paid _____

2016   **grenville & beatrice**
           best friends

"There is only one happiness in life, to
love & be loved." – George Sand

RETIRED FEBRUARY, 1994

COMMENTS: Issued January 1994, *Orig. S.R.* $26.00
🐾 Dove on the right front edge of the stones. First
editions were all that were produced. Dove was easily
broken off. Sought after by most collectors. (See next
entry below.)

1E $350 up

Have _____ Want_____ Price Paid _____

2016   **grenville & beatrice**
           best friends

"There is only one happiness in life, to
love & be loved." – George Sand

COMMENTS: Issued February 1994, Orig. S.R. $26.00
🐾 Appearing on 2Es, a dove is found on the center
front of stones. Perhaps a GRS, but not given GRS
status?

2E $65   **3E $60**   **4E up $26**

Have _____ Want_____ Price Paid _____

"I expect to pass through life but once. If, therefore, there be any
kindness I can show, or any good thing I can do to any fellow
being, let me do it now, and not defer or neglect it, as I shall not
pass this way again."

                     – William Penn

2017   **bailey & wixie**
              to have and to hold
              "Things are beautiful if you love them..."
              – Jean Anouith
COMMENTS: Issued January 1994, *Orig S.R.* $16.00
🐾 Such delicacy and beauty, a very precious piece.
1E $145   **2E $80**   **3E $50**
4E up $16
Have _____Want_____Price Paid _____

2018   **bailey & emily**
              forever friends
              "The only way to have a friend is to be
              one." – Emerson
              RETIRED DECEMBER, 1996
COMMENTS: Issued January 1994, *Orig. S.R.* $33.50
🐾 In version one *emily* has a pink bow, brown suit
and *bailey* has a pink dress. In version two, *emily* has
a blue bow, red suit and *bailey* has a blue dress. This
piece shows a bear and a hare together – what could
be more fun!
1E $125–145   **2E $75–80**   **3E up $60–65**
Have _____Want_____Price Paid _____

2019   **sherlock & watson**
              in disguise
              "Love Conquers All Things..." – Virgil
              RETIRED DECEMBER, 1996
COMMENTS: Issued January 1994, *Orig. S.R.* $16.00
🐾 No disguising this piece, it is delightful and special.
1E $120   **2E $60**   **3E $40**
4E up $16
Have _____Want_____Price Paid _____

Live so that you
wouldn't be ashamed to
sell the family parrot.

2020-06   **wilson**
at the beach
"Forget not that the Earth delights to feel your bare feet & the winds long to play with your hair..." – Gibran
TO BE RETIRED DECEMBER, 1997
COMMENTS: Issued January 1994, *Orig. S.R.* $16.00
🐾 Intricate piece. Same as *bailey at the beach* with color differences. Wilsons' hat and clothing are painted like a blue sailors suit.

| 1E $115 | 2E $50 | 3E $40 |
| 4E up $16 |

Have _____ Want_____ Price Paid _____

2020-09   **bailey**
at the beach
"Forget not that the Earth delights to feel your bare feet & the winds long to play with your hair." – Gibran
RETIRED DECEMBER, 1995
COMMENTS: Issued January 1994, *Orig. S.R.* $16.00
🐾 Same mold as 2020-6 *wilson at the beach*, except hat and clothing are painted pink. Some pieces were found with the item number being 2020.

| 1E $135–150 | 2E $70–80 | 3E up $45–50 |

Have _____ Want_____ Price Paid _____

2029-10   **juliette**
angel bear
"Light fades; the stars appear... evening angels gather near..."
RETIRED DECEMBER, 1995
COMMENTS: Issued January 1994, *Orig. S.R.* $13.00
🐾 This bear is light in color and is a mate to *clarence.*

| 1E $100 | 2E $60 | 3E up $50 |

Have _____ Want_____ Price Paid _____

2029-11   clarence   ☐
angel bear
"Light fades; the stars appear... evening angels gather near..."
RETIRED DECEMBER, 1995
COMMENTS: Issued January 1994, *Orig. S.R.* $13.00
🐾 Very popular bear.

1E $100	2E $60	3E up $50

Have _____Want_____Price Paid _____

2030   grenville   ☐
the Santa bear
"...hurt not the earth or the trees..."
RETIRED DECEMBER, 1996
COMMENTS: Issued January 1994, *Orig. S.R.* $14.50
🐾 Extremely hard to find. Some say it's most asked for in bear collection. Perhaps when pieces are retired we'll see edition sizes meaning less and less from 2E up, as one will buy them just to have the piece.

1E $475-$550	2E $350	3E up $250

Have _____Want_____Price Paid _____

2056(BC) lefty on the mound   ☐
"Never, never, never, never. give up"
– Winston Churchill
COMMENTS: Issued January 1995, *Orig. S.R.* $15.00
🐾 Canadian *lefty* is blue like the U.S. *lefty*. My piece has BC2056. (See page 20 for #2066 & #2253.)

1E $80	2E $35	3E $30
4E up $15		

Have _____Want_____Price Paid _____

2099   grenville & neville   ☐
the sign
COMMENTS: Issued June 1993, *Orig. S.R.* $16.00
🐾 This first version of the sign has no stamp numbers or edition numbers on the base, it was stained or brushed over with a brown color. Made for retailers only, but retailers sold it. Version two has a white base and no edition numbers.

Version 1: $125	Version 2: $16

Have _____Want_____Price Paid _____

2218   **homer on the plate**   ☐

*"Great works are performed not by
strength, but by perseverance."*
– Samuel Johnson

COMMENTS: Issued August 1994, *Orig. S.R.* $29.90
🐾 Produced exclusively for Canada and depicts the
Toronto Blue Jays. PLAY BALL! Get me a hot dog.

1E $90   **2E $45**   **3E $40**
4E up $29.90

Have _____Want_____Price Paid _____

2222   **wilson**   ☐
the perfesser

*"A teacher affects eternity; he can never
tell where his influence stops."*
– Henry Adams

TO BE RETIRED DECEMBER, 1997

COMMENTS: Issued January 1994, *Orig. S.R.* $16.50
🐾 A great teacher! Good ole "Mr. Wilson."

1E $95   **2E $60**   **3E $25**
4E up $16.50

Have _____Want_____Price Paid _____

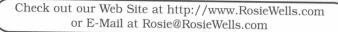

2223   **ted & teddy** ☐

"Love and the gentle heart are but a single thing." – Dante

TO BE RETIRED DECEMBER, 1997

COMMENTS: Issued January 1994, *Orig. S.R.* $16.00

🐾 Dad reading to son. A great piece.

1E $125   **2E $50**   **3E $35**

4E up $16

Have _____ Want _____ Price Paid _____

2225   **homer on the plate** ☐

"Great works are performed not by strength, but by perseverance."
– Samuel Johnson

COMMENTS: Issued January 1994, *Orig. S.R.* $16.00

🐾 Depicts America's favorite pastime.

1E $90   **2E $45**   **3E $30**

4E up $16

Have _____ Want _____ Price Paid _____

2226   **daphne** ☐

the reader hare

"He who has patience may accomplish anything." – Rabelais

COMMENTS: Issued January 1994, *Orig. S.R.* $14.50

🐾 Also called the "secrets of gardening" because her early boxes came with that inscription. A good candidate for retirement, in my opinion.

1E $115   **2E $65**   **3E $30**

4E up $14.50

Have _____ Want _____ Price Paid _____

Did You Know?

It's my opinion if any piece in these lines should be retired in 1997, add $50 to each price in this guide. Once these pieces become four or five years old, then due to larger production amounts I would only add $35 for insurance value. The more production, the less a search is needed and the secondary market is affected.

2227   **sebastian's prayer**   □
           golfer

"God is with those who persevere." – The Koran

RETIRED DECEMBER, 1996

COMMENTS: Issued January 1994, *Orig. S.R.* $16.50

🐾 Every golfer should have this piece.

1E $95   **2E $65**   **3E $55**

4E up $50

Have _____Want_____Price Paid _____

2228(CN)   **ewell & walton**   □
             manitoba mooselmen

"Caution...Always break for moose." – L. Smith

LIMITED EDITION

COMMENTS: Issued October 1996, *Orig. S.R.* $17.99
U.S. plus shipping, duty and handling.

🐾 Exclusive to Canada. Limited Edition figurine of
12,000 pieces. These figurines are numbered 1, 2, 3,
etc., but are not marked 1/12000, 2/12000. This was first
reported incorrectly to dealers as "manitoba moosemen."
There is an "l" in mooselmen. As of November, 1996, this
figurine was close to being sold out (almost as soon as it
debuted). Quite limited! Canadian retailers advertise
Boyds figurines in the *Collectors Bulletin*™ and *Weekly
Collectors' Gazette*™. Prices listed below are "predicted"
prices as of press time and may go higher.

#'s 1-100 $50   **101-300 $40**   **301-500 $35**

501-1000 $30   **1001-2000 $25**   **2001 up $20**

Have _____Want_____Price Paid _____

2229   **charlotte & bebe**   □
           the gardeners

*"If you truly love nature, you will find
beauty everywhere." –* Van Gogh

RETIRED DECEMBER, 1995

COMMENTS: Issued January 1994, *Orig. S.R.* $16.00

🐾 In high demand since its retirement.

1E $110   **2E $90**   **3E $70**

4E up $65

Have _____Want_____Price Paid _____

2230   **celeste** ☐
          the angel rabbit
          "To love is to receive a glimpse of heaven."
          – K. Sunde
COMMENTS: Issued January 1994, *Orig. S.R.* $16.50
🐾 A rare hare! Much sought after in 1E and 2E.
Some collect only the Boyds Hares!

1E $300	**2E $175**	**3E $115**

4E up $16.50
Have _____ Want _____ Price Paid _____

2231   **clara** ☐
          the nurse
          "... With gentle hands and a warm heart."
COMMENTS: Issued January 1994, *Orig. S.R.* $16.00
🐾 Very popular with people in the medical field.
Many nurses have this piece on shelves, not knowing
what they have! Earlier pieces 1E, 2E and 3E scarce.
Nice piece!

1E $325	**2E $170**	**3E $150**

4E up $16
Have _____ Want _____ Price Paid _____

2233   **grenville** ☐
          the graduate
          "Whatever you can do, or dream you can,
          begin it." – Goethe
          RETIRED DECEMBER, 1996
COMMENTS: Issued January 1994, *Orig. S.R.* $16.50
🐾 A great gift for the graduate. Reminds us all of that
special "Graduation Day." Usually girl graduate collectibles sell more as gift items than boy graduates. As
time goes by 1E – 2E prices will probably rise.

1E $100	**2E $70**	**3E $65**

4E up $65
Have _____ Want _____ Price Paid _____

2235   **kringle & bailey**
with list
"Love is the master key that opens the gates of happiness."
– Oliver Wendell Holmes
COMMENTS: Issued June 1994, *Orig. S.R.* $14.50
🐾 Sometimes "holiday related" collectibles do not rise on the secondary market as regular line pieces.

1E $85   **2E $50**   **3E $25**
4E up $14.50
Have _____Want_____Price Paid _____

2236   **elgin**
the elf bear
"God evidently does not intend us all to be rich, or powerful, or great but He does intend us all to be friends."
– Ralph Waldo Emerson
COMMENTS: Issued June 1994, *Orig. S.R.* $14.50
🐾 First of the elf bears.

1E $80   **2E $50**   **3E $25**
4E up $14.50
Have ___Want_____Price Paid _____

2237   **cookie**
the santa cat
"Love & Joy come to you..."
RETIRED DECEMBER, 1995
COMMENTS: Issued June 1994, *Orig. S.R.* $15.50
🐾 Another special piece for cat lovers.

1E $80   **2E $60**   **3E $55**
4E up $50
Have _____Want_____Price Paid _____

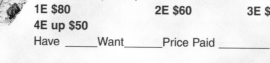

15

2238   **maynard**
            the santa moose
            "We shall find peace. We shall hear the
            Angels, we shall see the Sky Sparkling
            with Diamonds..."
COMMENTS: Issued June 1994, *Orig. S.R.* $15.50
🐾 A Christmas moose with style. A Santa, no less!
1E $80   **2E $50**   **3E $25**
4E up $15.50
Have _____Want_____Price Paid _____

2239   **bessie the santa cow**
            "Ho! Ho! Ho! Merry Chris-moo-s!"
            RETIRED DECEMBER, 1996
COMMENTS: Issued June 1994, *Orig S.R.* $16.00
🐾 Only cow in Bearstone collection. Cow collectors
love her!
1E $95   **2E $80**   **3E $70**
4E up $65
Have _____Want_____Price Paid _____

2240   **edmund & bailey**
            gathering holly
            "Friendship is the only cement that will
            ever hold the world together."
            – Woodrow Wilson
COMMENTS: Issued June 1994, *Orig. S.R.* $24.00
🐾 Super, super nice piece. Loved by all.
1E $160   **2E $70**   **3E $45**
4E up $24
Have _____Want_____Price Paid _____

Children are precious; enjoy.
Train up a child in the way he should
go: and when he is old, he will not
depart from it. Proverbs 22:6

2241   elliot & the tree   ☐

"The Holly's Up, the House is All Bright,
The Tree is Ready, the candles alight.
Rejoice & be glad all Children tonight!"
– P. Cornelius

COMMENTS: Issued June 1994, *Orig. S.R.* $16.50
🐾 Spectacular in detail and design. One of those "can't live without it" pieces. Merry Christmas!

1E $190	2E $85	3E $50

4E up $16.50

Have _____ Want_____ Price Paid _____

2242   elliot & the snowbeary   ☐

"The best portion of a good man's life, his little, nameless, unremembered acts of kindness & love." – William Woodworth

COMMENTS: Issued June 1994, *Orig. S.R.* $15.50
🐾 Snowbeary makes this outstanding. Great piece! A Teddy Bear Collectors' must have.

1E $90	2E $45	3E $30

4E up $15.50

Have _____ Want_____ Price Paid _____

2243   manheim
the eco-moose   ☐

"Woodman, Spare That Tree! Touch not a Single Bough! In Youth It Sheltered Me, And I'll Protect it Now."
– George Pope Morris

COMMENTS: Issued June 1994, *Orig. S.R.* $15.50
🐾 Second moose in collection! Great inspiration for an eco-moose!

1E $75	2E $35	3E $30

4E up $15.50

Have _____ Want_____ Price Paid _____

2245   **knute & the gridiron**   ☐

"Things may come to those who wait, but only the things left by those who hustle."
– Abraham Lincoln

COMMENTS: Issued June 1994, *Orig. S.R.* $16.50

🐾 A "tough" bear ready for action. Unusual name!

1E $80	2E $40	3E $28

4E up $16.50

Have _____ Want_____ Price Paid _____

2246   **agatha & shelly**   ☐
scaredy cat

"... the Gobble-uns 'll git you ef you Don't Watch Out!" – James Whitcomb Riley

COMMENTS: Issued June 1994, *Orig. S.R.* $14.50

🐾 1Es are scarce. Many collectors purchased this piece to add to their other Halloween Boyds collectibles. Cat collectors love her!

1E $75	2E $40	3E $30

4E up $14.50

Have _____ Want_____ Price Paid _____

2247   **hop-a-long**   ☐
the deputy

"Out where the handclasp's a little stronger, Out where the smile dwells a little longer, That's where the West begins."
– Arthur Chapman

COMMENTS: Issued January 1995, *Orig. S.R.* $14.00

🐾 A cowboy bear ready to ride the range. A great piece for retirement! (Just looks like one to have the honor!)

1E $60	2E $45	3E $22

4E up $14

Have _____ Want_____ Price Paid _____

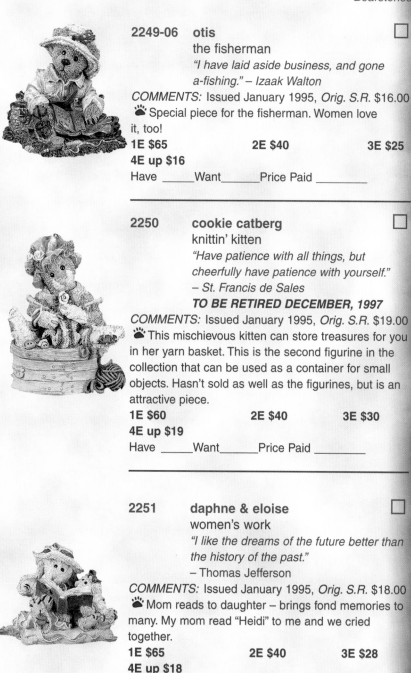

2249-06   **otis**   ☐
the fisherman
*"I have laid aside business, and gone
a-fishing." – Izaak Walton*
COMMENTS: Issued January 1995, *Orig. S.R.* $16.00
🐾 Special piece for the fisherman. Women love
it, too!
1E $65   **2E $40**   **3E $25**
4E up $16
Have _____Want_____Price Paid _____

2250   **cookie catberg**   ☐
knittin' kitten
*"Have patience with all things, but
cheerfully have patience with yourself."*
– St. Francis de Sales
TO BE RETIRED DECEMBER, 1997
COMMENTS: Issued January 1995, *Orig. S.R.* $19.00
🐾 This mischievous kitten can store treasures for you
in her yarn basket. This is the second figurine in the
collection that can be used as a container for small
objects. Hasn't sold as well as the figurines, but is an
attractive piece.
1E $60   **2E $40**   **3E $30**
4E up $19
Have _____Want_____Price Paid _____

2251   **daphne & eloise**   ☐
women's work
*"I like the dreams of the future better than
the history of the past."*
– Thomas Jefferson
COMMENTS: Issued January 1995, *Orig. S.R.* $18.00
🐾 Mom reads to daughter – brings fond memories to
many. My mom read "Heidi" to me and we cried
together.
1E $65   **2E $40**   **3E $28**
4E up $18
Have _____Want_____Price Paid _____

2252   **elf bear with list**   ☐

"He's making a list ... and checking it twice!"

LIMITED EDITION 1995

COMMENTS: Issued January 1995, *Orig. S.R.* $31.50
🐾 Scarce. The Canadian piece we have does not have a BC before its number. Does yours? Very hard to find. Sold only through the Carlton Cards stores in Canada. Limited to 1,865 pieces. Research found very few sales. Insure accordingly.

1E $300 up

Have _____ Want_____ Price Paid _____

2253   **lefty on the mound (For U.S.)**   ☐

2066   **lefty on the mound (For Canada)** ☐

"Never give in. Never, never, never, never."
– Winston Churchill

COMMENTS: Issued January 1995, *Orig. S.R.* $15.00
🐾 2253 was released for the U.S. market and 2066 was released for the Canadian market, as well as BC2056. The second number was reported in June of 1995. It has been stated that #2066 was supposed to be the Canadian number and that BC2056 should have never been released. (See pg. 10.) We've been told this hare is leaning on the wrong leg (turned wrong) to be a lefty pitcher. Oh boy!

1E $70   **2E $38**   **3E $25**
4E up $15

Have _____ Want_____ Price Paid _____

2254   **bailey**   ☐

the baker with sweetie pie

"Friends share all things." – Pythagoras

COMMENTS: Issued January 1995, *Orig. S.R.* $13.00
🐾 Cute gift to give to start a new collector! In my opinion, a great retirement candidate!!

1E $90   **2E $40**   **3E $30**
4E up $13

Have _____ Want_____ Price Paid _____

2254-cl   **bailey**   ☐
the baker with sweetie pie-clarion
SPECIAL EDITION
Teddy Bear Reunion in the Heartland 1995
Clarion, Iowa
RETIRED MARCH, 1995
COMMENTS: Issued March 1995, *Orig. S.R.* $18.00
🐾 Only 3,600 pieces were produced for this special
event in Clarion, Iowa. It is rumored that one hundred
of these were broken during shipping and were not
replaced, leaving 3,500 in existence. The only piece
marked Special Edition on bottom. "Clarion ❤ Iowa" is
printed on the pie. Many do not know about this piece.
1E $250
Have _____Want_____Price Paid _____

Do you spell that with a
"C" or a "K"?

The "Head Bean
Hisself" at his best while
signing for collectors. Ha!
That's "Gary"!

2255   **grenville & knute** ☐
football buddies
*"In life, as in a football game, the principle is:
Hit the Line Hard."* – Teddy Roosevelt
COMMENTS: Issued June 1995, *Orig. S.R.* $20.00
🐾 Another piece for the sports enthusiast.

1E $70   **2E $35**   **3E $25**
4E up $20
Have _____ Want _____ Price Paid _____

2256   **christmas big/little pig** ☐
*"In dreams and in love there are no
impossibilities."* – Janos Arany
RETIRED AUGUST, 1996
COMMENTS: Issued August 1994, *Orig. S.R.* $31.50
🐾 Exclusive to Canada. (Some may have 2256BC.)

1E $85   **2E $70**   **3E $60**
4E up $31.50
Have _____ Want _____ Price Paid _____

2258   **amelia's enterprise** ☐
carrot juice
*"A person's got to believe in something.
I believe I'll have another drink."*
– W.C. Fields
COMMENTS: Issued January 1995, *Orig. S.R.* $16.50
🐾 Drink up – carrot juice! One of the most popular of
the "hares." Hic!

1E $75   **2E $30**   **3E $22**
4E up $16.50
Have _____ Want _____ Price Paid _____

2259   **ms. bruin & bailey** ☐
the lesson

"The good teacher explains. The superior teacher demonstrates. The great teacher inspires." – Wm. Arthur Ward

"When you drink the water... Remember the spring." – Old Chinese Proverb

COMMENTS: Issued January 1995, *Orig. S.R.* $18.50

🐾 Voted **Figurine of the year in 1995** by NALED. A great piece!

1E $120   **2E $50**   **3E $28**
4E up $18.50

Have _____ Want_____ Price Paid _____

2260   **bailey** ☐
the honey bear

"Bee mine Honey."

COMMENTS: Issued January 1995, *Orig. S.R.* $16.00

🐾 A honey of a bear. A little bee buzzes on her hat.

1E $85   **2E $50**   **3E $25**
4E up $16

Have _____ Want_____ Price Paid _____

2261   **wilson** ☐
the wonderful wizard of wuzz

"We are all here for a spell; get all the good laughs you can." – Will Rogers

COMMENTS: Issued June 1995, *Orig. S.R.* $16.50

🐾 A very interesting, detailed piece. Even the quote draws your attention. The crystal ball makes for an outstanding look.

1E $55   **2E $30**   **3E $22**
4E up $16.50

Have _____ Want_____ Price Paid _____

What we call luck
Is simply pluck
And doing things over and over:
Courage and will,
Perseverance and skill,
Are the four leaves of luck's clover.
- Author Unknown

2262   **otis – tax time**   ☐

"The hardest thing in the world to understand is the income tax."
– Albert Einstein
"That money talks, I'll not deny. I heard it once... it said... goodbye..."
– Richard Armour

COMMENTS: Issued January 1995, *Orig. S.R.* $19.00
🐾 A great gift for the hard to buy for banker or tax consultant. Lots of detail. (Pictured on front cover.)

1E $65   **2E $45**   **3E $30**
4E up $19

Have _____ Want_____ Price Paid _____

2263   **union jack**   ☐
         love letters

"There are no warlike people... only warlike leaders." – Ralph Bunch

COMMENTS: June 1995, *Orig. S.R.* $19.00
🐾 Those people who are or have been in the military should admire this piece. Anyone who has ever been in the military or away from home should remember how special it felt to receive a letter from home.

1E $65   **2E $38**   **3E $25**
4E up $19

Have _____ Want_____ Price Paid _____

2265   **grenville**   ☐
         the storyteller
         LIMITED EDITION 1995

"We are all travellers in the wilderness of this world, and the best that we can hope to find in our travels is an honest friend."
– Robert Lewis Stevenson

COMMENTS: Issued June 1995, *Orig. S.R.* $44.95
🐾 The first Limited Edition Bearstone. Not marked by edition number, but by month – January through December. Due to the June debut, who can say which piece debuted first.

Sec. Mkt. Value: $75

Have _____ Want_____ Price Paid _____

2266   **angelica**   ☐
the guardian
"Mother is the name for God in the lips and hearts of children." – W.M. Thackeray
COMMENTS: Issued June 1995, *Orig. S.R.* $18.50
🐾 The cloud of this bear lifts off and you have a trinket box! Once a trinket box is retired maybe we will see more interest in them.

1E $72	2E $50	3E $28

4E up $18.50
Have _____ Want _____ Price Paid _____

2267   **simone & bailey**   ☐
helping hands
"The proper office of a friend is to side with you when you are in the wrong. Nearly anybody will side with you when you are in the right." – Mark Twain
COMMENTS: Issued June 1995, *Orig. S.R.* $26.00
🐾 A nice gift for your best friend. The ice is produced in a clear resin like substance for a clever effect!

1E $58	2E $40	3E $35

4E up $26
Have _____ Want _____ Price Paid _____

2268   **bailey**   ☐
the cheerleader
"Nothing great was ever achieved without enthusiasm." – Ralph Waldo Emerson
COMMENTS: Issued June 1995, *Orig. S.R.* $16.00
🐾 A favorite among the younger crowd.

1E $55	2E $40	3E $25

4E up $16
Have _____ Want _____ Price Paid _____

2269   **emma**
the witchy bear
"With mirth and laughter, let old wrinkles come." – Thomas Hardy
COMMENTS: Issued June 1995, *Orig. S.R.* $17.50
🐾 An amusing figurine to display in a prominent spot at Halloween or anytime.

1E $65   **2E $50**   **3E $40**
4E up $17.50
Have _____Want_____Price Paid _____

2272   **bailey**
hearts desire
"Love comforteth like sunshine after rain." – Shakespeare
COMMENTS: Issued January 1996, *Orig. S.R.* $15.00
🐾 Many sweethearts received this piece as a Valentine gift.

1E $90   **2E $50**   **3E $35**
4E up $15
Have _____Want_____Price Paid _____

2273   **justina**
message bearer
"I have never been able to understand why it is that just because I am unintelligible nobody understands me." – Milton Mayer
COMMENTS: Issued January 1996, *Orig. S.R.* $16.00
🐾 Another fine piece to own. Comes with two signs which are removable. On one sign it says, "I love U" and on the other side it says, "I'm Sorry." The other sign says, "Thanks" and on the reverse side it says, "Congrats."

1E $50   **2E $25**   **3E $22**
4E up $16
Have _____Want_____Price Paid _____

2274   **grenville & beatrice**   ☐
         true love

"The great secret of successful marriage is to treat all disasters as incidents and none of the incidents as disaster." – Harold Nicholson

COMMENTS: Issued January 1996, *Orig. S.R.* $36.00
🐾 Great wedding cake topper. Collector reports this piece has been found with an error. The words "RUE LOVE" are found on sign above couple. Other noticeable differences can been seen on the picture of "RUE LOVE" found on page X.

1E $95   **2E $70**   **3E $55**
4E up $36
Have _____Want_____Price Paid _____

2275   **m. harrison's birthday**   ☐

"Whatever you are, be a good one." – Lincoln

COMMENTS: Issued January 1996, *Orig. S.R.* $17.00

1E $55   **2E $30**   **3E $22**
4E up $17
Have _____Want_____Price Paid _____

2276   **ms. griz (pink)**   ☐
         monday morning

"You have to accept whatever comes, and the only important thing is that you meet it with the best you have to give." – Eleanor Roosevelt

COMMENTS: Issued January 1996, *Orig. S.R.* $34.00
🐾 First produced in pink dress. *ms. griz* showed up at work first in a pink dress. Later she changed into a blue dress. Her most sought after attire by avid collectors is the pink dress. I do not know exactly when the blue dress debuted or in which edition it began. Do you have a blue dress in 1E, 2E, etc.? Let me know. How far into the production did "pinkie" go? Collector comments welcome! I have her in a 4E. I look for "pinkie" *ms. griz* to continue to increase in value if not produced for more than four or five editions.

1E $125 up   **2E up $120 up**
Have _____Want_____Price Paid _____

2276   **ms. griz (blue)**   ☐
monday morning

*"You have to accept whatever comes, and
the only important thing is that you meet it
with the best you have to give."*
– Eleanor Roosevelt

COMMENTS: Issued January 1996, *Orig. S.R.* $34.00
🐾 Mr. Lowenthal intended *ms. griz* to be dressed in
blue originally.

1E $85	2E $40	3E $34
4E up $34		

Have _____ Want_____ Price Paid _____

2277   **emma & bailey**   ☐
afternoon tea

*"Friendship improves happiness and
abates misery, by doubling our joy, and
dividing our grief."* – Addison

COMMENTS: Issued January 1996, *Orig. S.R.* $18.00
🐾 Can't you hear their chitter-chatter?!

1E $80	2E $65	3E $45
4E up $18		

Have _____ Want_____ Price Paid _____

2278   **noah & co.**   ☐
ark builders
LIMITED EDITION, 1996

*"I have yet to find the man, however exalted
his station... who did not do better work and
put forth greater effort under a spirit of
approval than under a spirit of criticism."*
– Charles Schwab

*"We didn't all come over on the same ship,
but we're all in the same boat."*
– Bernard M. Baruch

COMMENTS: Issued August 1996, *Orig. S.R.* $60.00
🐾 This piece was a limited edition figurine marked by
the month just as 2265 *grenville... storyteller.* No idea
as to how many were produced.

Sec. Mkt. Value: $115-$125

Have _____ Want_____ Price Paid _____

2279   **sir edmund**   □
persistence

"I always remember an epitaph... 'Here lies Jake Williams. He done his damnedest.' I think that is the greatest epitaph a man can have - when he gives everything that is in him to do the job he has before him." – Harry S. Truman

COMMENTS: Issued Fall 1996, *Orig. S.R.* $21.00

🐾 A favorite of all here at Rosie Wells Enterprises, Inc. The October/November issue of the *Collectors' Bulletin*™ featured this figurine on the front cover. Here at Rosie Wells Enterprises it's our opinion this could become the most favorite of all the li'l bears produced to date! G-R-E-A-T Piece! Perfect for a man's gift, too! Look for our art design of *sir edmund* on the next Boyds' catalog! Ta Da!

1E $95   **2E $50**   **3E $28**
4E up $21
Have _____ Want _____ Price Paid _____

2280   **elliot**   □
the hero

"Nothing is so strong as gentleness, nothing so gentle as real strength."
– Francis de Sales

COMMENTS: Issued Fall 1996, *Orig. S.R.* $17.00

🐾 This piece has an error and we have not heard of it being corrected to date. It reads the "Beatstone Collection" instead of Bearstone Collection. No real significance in my opinion for a big secondary market value find. Isn't this a super piece?!

1E $65   **2E $40**   **3E $25**
4E up $17
Have _____ Want _____ Price Paid _____

Did You Know?

There are approximately 6,050 Boyds & Friends retailers as of early 1997! It's been said by top ranking folks that there are approximately 200,000 buyers of these pieces! 1E through 4Es at 3,600 per edition adds up to only 14,400 pieces! Not a high number when considering the 200,000 buyers!!

2281   **grenville with matthew & bailey** ☐
sunday afternoon

"We should never despair; our situation before has been unpromising and has changed for the better, so I trust, it will again." – George Washington
"Growing old is not for sissies."
– Bette Davis

COMMENTS: Issued Fall 1996, *Orig. S.R.* $35.00
🐾 Checkers anyone?

1E $85	2E $50	3E $40
4E up $35		

Have _____ Want _____ Price Paid _____

2282   **momma mcbear** ☐
anticipation

"Grace was in her steps, heav'n in her eyes..." – John Milton

COMMENTS: Issued Fall 1996, *Orig. S.R.* $15.00
🐾 Perfect for the new mom-to-be. A great gift to give hubby to announce the big event.

1E $48	2E $30	3E $25
4E up $15		

Have _____ Want _____ Price Paid _____

2283   **kringle & company** ☐

"What we love we shall grow to resemble."
– St. Bernard

COMMENTS: Issued Fall 1996, *Orig. S.R.* $18.00
🐾 Notice the red outfit? Does this inscription mean I'm going to look like a large pizza some day?

1E $45	2E $38	3E $25
4E up $18		

Have _____ Want _____ Price Paid _____

2283-01 kringle & company ☐

"What we love we shall grow to resemble."
– St. Bernard
GCC EXCLUSIVE
COMMENTS: Issued Fall 1996, *Orig. S.R.* $18.00
🐾 This exclusive GCC figurine was available with color changes November 16, 1996. GCC will be printed on the bottom of the GCC pieces. Notice the green outfit?

GCC 1E $45 up   2E $35   3E up $25
Have _____Want_____Price Paid _____

2284 ms. griz...saturday night ☐

"A moment on the lips, a lifetime on the hips."
– Smith & Murray
GCC EXCLUSIVE
COMMENTS: Issued Fall 1996, Orig. S.R. $15.00
🐾 A special exclusive GCC figurine. Sure to be a special one to own. Another quotation regarding my beloved pizzas!

GCC 1E $40 up   2E $30   3E up $25
Have _____Want_____Price Paid _____

Holiday Pageant

According to Boyds, the Holiday Pageant will continue with pieces to be introduced through 1999. In 1995 the first four pieces were introduced. In 1996 four more were introduced. In 1997 there will possibly be seven pieces introduced and in 1998 there will possibly be eight new styles introduced! In 1999 the entire Holiday Pageant will be produced for the last time and then on December 31, 1999, the molds will be broken. Edition sizes for each piece are 7,200, not 3,600 as in other sizes!

2401 neville ☐
as joseph
"Peace to him that is far off, and to him that is near." – Isaiah 57:19
COMMENTS: Issued June 1995, *Orig. S.R.* $15.00
🐾

1E $30   2E $22   3E up $15
Have _____Want_____Price Paid _____

2402   **theresa**   ☐
as mary
"Before honor is humility."
– Proverbs 15:33
COMMENTS: Issued June 1995, *Orig. S.R.* $15.00
🐾

1E $30   **2E $22**   **3E up $15**
Have _____Want_____Price Paid _____

2403   **baldwin**   ☐
as the child
"Unto us a child is born, Unto us a Son is given." – Handel's *Messiah*
COMMENTS: Issued June 1995, *Orig. S.R.* $15.00
🐾 It is my opinion we may see larger edition sizes as production is planned through 1999. Nativities are a popular collectible.

1E $35   **2E $20**   **3E up $15**
Have _____Want_____Price Paid _____

2404   **wilson**   ☐
as melchior
"I find nothing so dear as that which is given me." – Montaigne
COMMENTS: Issued January 1996, *Orig. S.R.* $15.00
🐾

1E $30   **2E $20**   **3E $18**
4E up $15
Have _____Want_____Price Paid _____

2405   **heath**   ☐
as casper
"All wisdom is summed up in two words – Wait and Hope." – Dumas
COMMENTS: Issued January 1996, *Orig. S.R.* $15.00
🐾

1E $30   **2E $20**   **3E $18**
4E up $15
Have _____Want_____Price Paid _____

2406   **raleigh**   ☐
         as balthasar

"An honest man's the noblest work of God."
– Alexander Pope

COMMENTS: Issued January 1996, *Orig. S.R.* $15.00

1E $30   **2E $20**   **3E $18**
4E up $15
Have _____Want_____Price Paid _____

2407   **thatcher & eden**   ☐
         as the camel

"Coming together is a beginning; keeping together is progress; working together is success." – Henry Ford

COMMENTS: Issued January 1996, *Orig. S.R.* $18.00

1E $25   **2E $20**   **3E up $18**
Have _____Want_____Price Paid _____

2425   **the stage – school pageant**   ☐

"We spend our years as a tale that is told." – Psalms 90:9

COMMENTS: Issued June 1995, *Orig. S.R.* $34.50

1E $40   **2E $34.50**
3E up $34.50
Have _____Want_____Price Paid _____

Editor's Note

Could not find any sales on the secondary market for these pieces.
With 7,200 per edition, I suggest you insure at these prices.
It will take longer for these to increase on the secondary market,
in my opinion. These prices are only my suggestion of value in
order to insure.

Ornaments

2500   faith ☐
angel bear with trumpet
RETIRED DECEMBER 31, 1996
COMMENTS: Issued 1994, *Orig. S.R.* $10.00
🐾 There were no edition numbers on this ornament –
no space. By mid 1997 may be selling for $18-$20.
Have _____Want_____Price Paid _____

2501   hope ☐
angel bear with wreath
RETIRED DECEMBER 31, 1996
COMMENTS: Issued 1994, *Orig. S.R.* $10.00
🐾 No edition numbers. Insure for $18-$20.
Have _____Want_____Price Paid _____

2502   charity ☐
angel bear with star
RETIRED DECEMBER 31, 1996
COMMENTS: Issued 1994, *Orig. S.R.* $10.00
🐾 No edition numbers. Insure for $18-$22.
Have _____Want_____Price Paid _____

2505   edmund ☐
"believe"
COMMENTS: Issued 1995, *Orig. S.R.* $10.00
🐾 No edition numbers. Insure for $10.
Have _____Want_____Price Paid _____

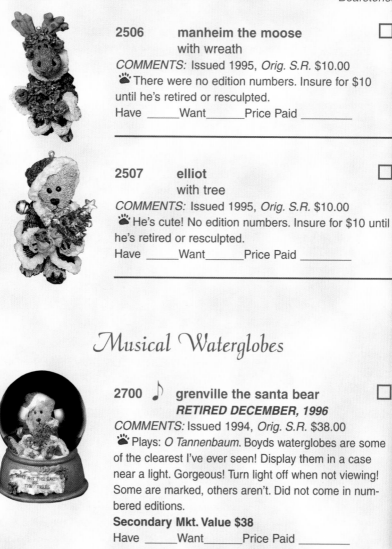

2506   **manheim the moose**   ☐
      with wreath
COMMENTS: Issued 1995, *Orig. S.R.* $10.00
🐾 There were no edition numbers. Insure for $10 until he's retired or resculpted.
Have _____ Want _____ Price Paid _____

2507   **elliot**   ☐
      with tree
COMMENTS: Issued 1995, *Orig. S.R.* $10.00
🐾 He's cute! No edition numbers. Insure for $10 until he's retired or resculpted.
Have _____ Want _____ Price Paid _____

Musical Waterglobes

2700 ♪ **grenville the santa bear**   ☐
      RETIRED DECEMBER, 1996
COMMENTS: Issued 1994, *Orig. S.R.* $38.00
🐾 Plays: *O Tannenbaum.* Boyds waterglobes are some of the clearest I've ever seen! Display them in a case near a light. Gorgeous! Turn light off when not viewing! Some are marked, others aren't. Did not come in numbered editions.
Secondary Mkt. Value $38
Have _____ Want _____ Price Paid _____

2702 ♪ **angelicia the guardian angel**   ☐
COMMENTS: Issued 1995, *Orig. S.R.* $37.00
🐾 Plays: *I'll Always Love You*
Does not come in numbered editions.
Secondary Mkt. Value $37
Have _____ Want _____ Price Paid _____

2704 ♪ elliot & the tree ☐

COMMENTS: Issued 1995, *Orig. S.R.* $35.00
🐾 Plays: *I'll Be Home For Christmas.*
Does not come in numbered editions.
Secondary Mkt. Value $35
Have _____ Want _____ Price Paid _____

2705 ♪ simone & bailey ☐

COMMENTS: Issued 1996, *Orig. S.R.* $35.00
🐾 Plays: *Skater's Waltz*
The first Boyds musical to come with numbered editions!

1E $50   **2E $40**   **3E up $35**
Have _____ Want _____ Price Paid _____

2706 ♪ noah & co. ☐
LIMITED EDITION – ONE PER RETAILER

COMMENTS: Issued 1996, Orig. S.R. $51.00

🐾 Limited to 6,144 pieces. The Boyds Company offered 144 pieces to their employees. Marked by number and edition size on the base. Musicals purchased in Canada were marked with a <u>c</u> before the edition number. We have heard low numbers went to Canada. Plays *Singing In The Rain.* A beautiful waterglobe. Quality plus! Watch this waterglobe to become a favorite and very sought after in my opinion. Some say this could go higher and higher. Time will tell. These debuted mid October 1996. I saw two sell at our show in October, 1996, for $125 and $140. I would insure for $500 after June, 1997. May go higher – maybe not. We'll keep you informed in the *Weekly Collectors' Gazette*™, *Collectors' Bulletin*™ and Hot Line.

Collectors are not seeking out any number; they're just glad to get the musical. Should you find one numbered under 500, it would be considered a very desirable musical for the avid collector to own.
Have _____ Want _____ Price Paid _____

Votive

2770 emma the witchy bear
pumpkin magic

"...And listen to their marvelous tales of Ghosts and Goblins, and Haunted Brooks, and Haunted Bridges and Haunted Houses..." – Washington Irving

COMMENTS: Issued 1996, *Orig. S.R.* $26.00

🐾 Don't miss out on these votives! You'll really enjoy them! I do!

1E $60   **2E $40**   **3E $35**
4E up $26

Have _____Want_____Price Paid _____

2771 elgin & elliot the elves
toasty warm

"There is no place more delightful than one's own fireplace."

COMMENTS: Issued 1996, *Orig. S.R.* $26.00

🐾 The votive glass inside the chimney is red. So special when lit! Just love mine! Get one!

1E $60   **2E $45**   **3E $40**
4E up $26

Have _____Want_____Price Paid _____

2772 edmund the elf bear
holiday glow

"I was the night before Christmas and all through the house..."

"T'was the night before Christmas and all through the house..." – Clement Moore

COMMENTS: Issued 1996, *Orig. S.R.* $26.00

🐾 In the first edition of this votive the quote started with "I." Somewhere in the third edition it was changed to "T'was." Sooo cute!

1E $65   **2E $50**   **3E $40**
4E up $26

Have _____Want_____Price Paid _____

In my opinion, some have overlooked buying these votives.
If they retire, the search would be on!!

Shoe Box Bears

Moveable arms and legs on rubber bands. To pose bear, pull the leg out gently to avoid scratching paint. Do not twist! Hopefully the rubber bands will last…
"First" Shoe Box Bears may go higher in '97.

3200   augustus "gus" grizberg ☐

COMMENTS: Issued 1996, *Orig. S.R.* $19.00

🐾 Shoe Box Bears™ – First introduced nationwide on QVC and were marked "Q96" inside the leg. Later editions were marked 1E, 2E, etc., on the inner leg for retail sales in edition sizes of 6,000! Not as scarce as the figurines. Because it was difficult to mark the inner leg, a certificate with the edition and piece number will be enclosed in the box, not on the bears. It is not clear how many editions will be marked before they change to certificates.

Q96 $40 up   1E $25 up   2E up $19
Certificate # $19
Have _____ Want_____ Price Paid _____

3201   gertrude "gertie" grizberg ☐

COMMENTS: Issued 1996, *Orig. S.R.* $14.50

🐾 Shoe Box Bears™ – First marked "Q96"; later editions were marked 1E, 2E, etc., for retail sales. Because it was difficult to mark the inner leg, a certificate with the edition and piece number will be enclosed in the box. It is not clear how many editions will be marked before they change to certificates.

Q96 $40 up   1E $25
2E up $14.50   Certificate # $14.50
Have _____ Want_____ Price Paid _____

3201-01   gladys grizberg ☐

COMMENTS: Issued 1996, *Orig. S.R.* $15.00

🐾 Exclusive NALED catalog bear. Similar to *gertie* (3201) except she will have a pink bow and will be lighter in color. NALED Catalog, GCC, Palmer and Parade of Gifts are catalogs for participating dealers. It will be interesting to see how long rubber bands on legs will wear and last.

1E $35 up   2E up $15
Certificate # $15
Have _____ Want_____ Price Paid _____

3202　　thaddeus "bud" grizberg　☐

COMMENTS: Issued 1996, *Orig. S.R.* $10.00

🐾 Shoe Box Bears™ – Marked in the same fashion as *gertie* and *gus.*

Q96 $25　　　　　**1E $18**　　　　　**2E $10**

Certificate # $10

Have ＿＿＿Want＿＿＿Price Paid ＿＿＿＿

Ornaments

25700　　edmund

　　　　　with wreath　☐

COMMENTS: Issued 1996, *Orig. S.R.* $11.00

🐾 Different! Cute!

1E $25　　　　　**2E $15**　　　　　**3E $12**

4E up $11

Have ＿＿＿Want＿＿＿Price Paid ＿＿＿＿

25701　　clair with gingerbread man　☐

COMMENTS: Issued 1996, *Orig. S.R.* $11.00

🐾 Will sit on shelf, too. Unusual in looks!

1E $25　　　　　**2E $15**　　　　　**3E $12**

4E up $11

Have ＿＿＿Want＿＿＿Price Paid ＿＿＿＿

25702　　wilson with shooting star　☐

COMMENTS: Issued 1996, *Orig. S.R.* $11.00

🐾 Different ... look for these three '96 ornaments.

1E $25　　　　　**2E $15**　　　　　**3E $12**

4E up $11

Have ＿＿＿Want＿＿＿Price Paid ＿＿＿＿

bailey & matthew
LIMITED EDITION

COMMENTS: Issued 1996, *Orig. S.R.* $70.00

🐾 1996 Limited Edition offered on QVC. Came in set with two plush bears, *bailey* and *matthew*. A retailer reported ordering and receiving just the plush. A collector reported buying this set from a retailer before QVC offering. Also have been made available in a national gift catalog. Insure ornaments for $20 each until more is learned on quantities produced, etc.

Have _____Want_____Price Paid _____

The Loyal Order of Friends of Boyds

01996-21 uncle elliot
... the head bean wants you!

"... I don't care to belong to any club that will accept me as a member."
– Groucho Marx

COMMENTS: Issued 1996, *Orig. S.R.* $30.00

🐾 Available only with club membership. The official membership drive was launched on August 1, 1996. Kits were shipped on or around October, 1996. Kits included *uncle elliot*, *raeburn* (a 6" distressed plush grizzly bear) and *uncle elliot* (a patriotic Bearstone™ pin). In Spring of 1997 collectors will have the opportunity to purchase "Original F.o.B." members only pieces. Also stamped on the bottom of this piece is "Special F.o.B. 1996 – 1997 Edition." Charter membership available until December, 1997. Pick up a form at your Boyds dealer. This would be a great piece to have signed by Gary. He will be at the International Collectible Expo in Long Beach, CA, on April 19 & 20 and at Rosemont, IL on June 28 & 29. Look for our booth, too! I'll be there with a special memento!

Have _____Want_____Price Paid _____

The San Francisco Music Box Company
proudly presents
Boyds Bears & Friends™...The Bearstone Collection

2700-SF ♪ **grenville the santa bear** ☐

COMMENTS: Issued 1996, *Orig. S.R.* $44.95

🐾 Plays: *When You Wish Upon A Star.* These water-globes are one of the clearest I've seen. The "twinkle" of the snow is quality plus!

1E $65   **2E $55**   **3E $48**
4E up $45

Have _____ Want_____ Price Paid _____

2701-SF ♪ **ted & teddy** ☐

COMMENTS: Issued 1995, *Orig. S.R.* $44.95

🐾 There were two different versions made of this waterglobe. The first version had a misspelled label that read "THE BODYS COLLECTION"; it also played *For The Good Times.* The second version has a corrected label and now plays *Teddy Bear's Picnic.* The bottom log appears thicker and the print on the pages is not as vivid.

Version 1:1E $125   **2E $95**   **3E $50**
4E up $45
Version 2: 1E $55   **2E $48**   **3E up $45 up**

Have _____ Want_____ Price Paid _____

2703-SF ♪ **santa's flight plan** ☐

COMMENTS: Issued 1996, *Orig. S.R.* $44.95

🐾 Plays: *Santa Claus Is Coming To Town.*

1E $60   **2E $50**   **3E up $45**

Have _____ Want_____ Price Paid _____

2704-SF ♪ elliot & the tree ☐

COMMENTS: Issued 1996, *Orig. S.R.* $44.95

🐾 Plays: *I'll Be Home For Christmas.*

1E $60	2E $48	3E up $45

Have _____ Want _____ Price Paid _____

2750-SF ♪ wilson & the love sonnets ☐

COMMENTS: Issued 1995, *Orig. S.R.* $39.95

🐾 Two different versionsof this music box have been produced. Version one plays *Your're Nobody Till Somebody Loves You* and has a one piece mold with the misspelled label. This piece is also much larger than the second version. Version two is a two piece mold that has many noticeable changes. The first of these is the fact that his sweater is lower to allow his head to move easier. The label has been corrected and the new tune is *Memory.*

Version 1: 1E $145	2E $90	3E $50
4E up $40		
Version 2: 1E $85	2E $50	3E up $45

Have _____ Want _____ Price Paid _____

2751-SF ♪ grenville (arthur) on trunk ☐

COMMENTS: Issued 1995, *Orig. S.R.* $39.95

🐾 *Let Me Be Your Teddy Bear* is played by the first version of this music box. It also has the misspelled label and is slightly larger than version two. Version two plays the same tune but there are some noted changes. The bottom of the piece is not painted, there is no paw print on the patch on the scarf and his right leg has © 1995 TBC.

Version 1: 1E $125	2E $50	3E up $40
Version 2: 1E $50	2E $45	3E up $40

Have _____ Want _____ Price Paid _____

2752-SF ♪ **emma & bailey tea party** ☐

COMMENTS: Issued November 1996, *Orig. S.R.* $44.95
🐾 Plays: *Tea For Two.*
Secondary market value not established to date.
Have _____ Want _____ Price Paid _____

2753-SF ♪ **clarence angel** ☐

COMMENTS: Issued November 1996, *Orig. S.R.* $39.95
🐾 Plays: *When You Wish Upon A Star.*
Secondary market value not established to date.
Have _____ Want _____ Price Paid _____

2754-SF ♪ **neville bedtime** ☐

COMMENTS: Issued November 1996, *Orig. S.R.* $39.95
🐾 Plays: *A Dream Is A Wish Your Heart Makes.*
Secondary market value not established to date.
Have _____ Want _____ Price Paid _____

2755-SF ♪ bailey with suitcase ☐
COMMENTS: Issued November 1996, *Orig. S.R.* $39.95
🐾 Plays: *Let Me Be Your Teddy Bear.* I expect only
1Es to be on secondary market in early 1997.
Secondary market value not established to date.
Have _____ Want _____ Price Paid _____

2756-SF ♪ ms. bruin & bailey school ☐
COMMENTS: Issued November 1996, *Orig. S.R.* $39.95
🐾 Plays: *Getting To Know You.*
Secondary market value not established to date.
Have _____ Want _____ Price Paid _____

2757-SF ♪ bailey & emily picnic ☐
COMMENTS: Issued November 1996, *Orig. S.R.* $39.95
🐾 Plays: *Teddy Bear's Picnic.*
1E $55   **2E $45**   **3E $40**
4E up $40
Have _____ Want _____ Price Paid _____

2267-SF ♪ skating bears ☐
COMMENTS: Issued 1996, *Orig. S.R.* $44.95
🐾 Plays: *Skater's Waltz.*
Secondary market value not established to date.
Have _____ Want _____ Price Paid _____

Pat's Pin Collection

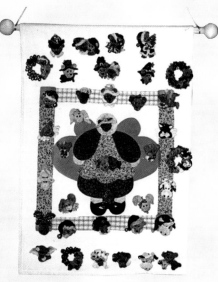

Pat Santos & Rosie

Pat says:

"I enjoy collecting the Boyds Bearwear Pins. You can choose one to wear for almost any occasion. When you wear one and walk into a store or any public place, someone is sure to admire your pin. Most of them are Bearstone Collectors and will strike up a conversation just because you wear a pin. It's fun! An easy way to meet new people and talk about bears."

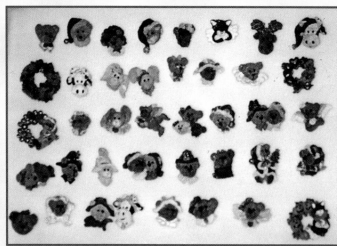

"Look for the Boyds Name."

FOLKSTONES™

None can compare to these tall li'l dudes! A delightful whimsical look that will always make you smile no matter how you feel! Don't pass them by! Each edition size in the Folkstone collection consists of 3,600 pieces.

2703 ♪ **santa & friends** ☐
santa's flight plan
COMMENTS: Issued 1996, *Orig. S.R.* $38.00
🌲Plays: *Santa Claus Is Coming To Town.*

1E $125	2E $75	3E $40
4E up $38		

Have _____ Want _____ Price Paid _____

2710 **jean claude & jacque** ☐
snowmen skiers
"Let it Snow"
COMMENTS: Issued Fall 1996, *Orig. S.R.* $38.00
🌲 Reported error found on the bottom of this water-globe. Inscription reads *"Lte it Snow."*

1E $115	2E $60	3E $40
4E up $38		

Have _____ Want _____ Price Paid _____

2800 **nicholai** ☐
with tree
"Yes, Virginia, there is a Santa Claus..."
– Editorial, The New York Sun – 1897
COMMENTS: Issued September 1994, *Orig. S.R.* $17.00
☆

1E $75	2E $35	3E $25
4E up $17		

Have _____ Want _____ Price Paid _____

2801   nikki   ☐
with candle
"A candle loses nothing of its light by lighting another candle."
COMMENTS: Issued September 1994, *Orig. S.R.* $17.00
☆

1E $70	2E $30	3E $22
4E up $17		

Have _____ Want _____ Price Paid _____

2802   nicholas   ☐
with book list
"He's making a list... and checking it twice!"
COMMENTS: Issued September 1994, *Orig. S.R.* $17.00
☆

1E $75	2E $30	3E $22
4E up $17		

Have _____ Want _____ Price Paid _____

2803   slik nick   ☐
the chimney sweep
"Nothing is impossible to a willing heart."
– John Heywood
COMMENTS: Issued August 1995, *Orig. S.R.* $18.00
☆There are two versions of this figurine. Version one is the older, more sought after figurine. Version two is the GRS (General Resculptured) Edition. Actually, the first version's molds were worn out and new ones were made. Only Folkstones and Santa & Friends have GRS (General Resculptured).

Orig. 1E $55	2E $40	3E $30
4E up $18		
GRS Ed.: 1E $30	2E $25	3E $22
4E up $18		

Have _____ Want _____ Price Paid _____

2804 na-nick of the north ☐

"Nature is full of genius... so that not a snowflake escapes its fashioning hand."
– Thoreau

COMMENTS: Issued August 1995, *Orig. S.R.* 18.00
☆There are two versions for this figurine as well. The original, which is version one, and the GRS Edition which is version two.

Orig: 1E $55	**2E $40**	**3E $30**
4E up $18		
GRS Ed.: 1E $35	**2E $25**	**3E $20**
4E up $18		

Have _____Want_____Price Paid _____

2805 no-no nick ☐
bad boy santa

"Never take anything for granted."
– Benjamin Disraeli

COMMENTS: Issued Fall 1996, *Orig. S.R.* $18.00
☆Collect all the Santas; you'll be glad you did!

1E $45	**2E $30**	**3E $20**
4E up $18		

Have _____Want_____Price Paid _____

2806 nicknoah ☐
santa with ark

"Little friends may prove great friends."
– Aesop

COMMENTS: Issued Fall 1996, *Orig. S.R.* $18.00
☆

1E $45	**2E $30**	**3E $20**
4E up $18		

Have _____Want_____Price Paid _____

2807   nanick & siegfried
the plan
LIMITED EDITION

COMMENTS: Issued Fall 1996, *Orig. S.R.* $33.00
★This is the first truly limited figurine from Boyds and production is limited to 10,000 pieces. Supplies are very limited so hurry before they are all gone! Once all 10,000 pieces are produced, all of the molds will be broken and this piece will never be made again. There is no quote on the bottom of this figurine. Only number 1-10,000. Bottom stamped & numbered 1/10,000, 2/10,000, etc. Figurines from Canada marked with a "C" before the edition number.

#1-100 $150	**101-200 $135**	**201-500 $120**
501-1000 $115	**1001 up $75**	

Have _____ Want_____ Price Paid _____

2808   st. nick
the quest
"He was not of an age, but for all time."
– Shakespeare
GCC EXCLUSIVE

COMMENTS: Issued 1996, *Orig. S.R.* $20.00
★This is a GCC Exclusive figurine.

GCC 1E $40	**2E $25**	**3E up $20**

Have _____ Want_____ Price Paid _____

2810   windy
with book
"In Dreams and in Love there are no impossibilities." – Janus Arany
RETIRED DECEMBER, 1996

COMMENTS: Issued September 1994, *Orig. S.R.* $17.00
★Among the first in this line. Very popular!!

1E $90	**2E $55**	**3E $45**
4E $40	**5E up $35**	

Have _____ Want_____ Price Paid _____

2811   chilly & son   ☐
with dove
"Repeat the Sounding Joys..."
COMMENTS: Issued September 1994, *Orig. S.R.* $17.00
☆Came with the group of the very first pieces! Was an instant hit!

1E $70   **2E $50**   **3E $30**
4E up $25
Have _____ Want_____ Price Paid _____

2812   jingles & son   ☐
with wreath
"Do not squander time, for it is the stuff life is made of." – Benjamin Franklin
RETIRED DECEMBER, 1996
COMMENTS: Issued September 1994, *Orig. S.R.* $17.00
☆So, so great – was one of the first! Not as popular as *windy* (2810).

1E $85   **2E $65**   **3E $60**
4E up $55
Have _____ Want_____ Price Paid _____

2814   northbound willie   ☐
"The fool wanders, the wiseman travels."
– Thomas Fuller
COMMENTS: Issued August 1995, *Orig. S.R.* $17.00
☆Two different versions of this figurine have been found. Version one is the original mold. The second version is the GRS Edition.

Version 1: 1E $48   **2E $30**   **3E $22**
4E up $18
GRS Ed.: 1E $25   **2E $21**   **3E up $17**
Have _____ Want_____ Price Paid _____

2815   **jean claude & jacques**   ☐

"The Northwind shall blow, and we shall have snow..." – Old Nursery Rhyme

COMMENTS: Issued August 1995, *Orig. S.R.* $17.00
☆There are two different versions of this figurine. Version one is the original mold. After changes were made the second version was released which is the GRS Edition.

Version 1: 1E $50   **2E $35**   **3E $25**
4E up $22
GRS Ed.: 1E $22   **2E $20**   **3E up $17**
Have _____Want_____Price Paid _____

2816   **robin**   ☐
the snowbird lover

"All who would win joy, must share it..."
– Lord Byron

COMMENTS: Issued Fall 1996, *Orig. S.R.* $18.00
☆
1E $40   **2E $25**   **3E $20**
4E up $18
Have _____Want_____Price Paid _____

2817   **nanny**   ☐
the snowman

"Life is a great bundle of little things."
– Oliver Wendell Holmes

COMMENTS: Issued Fall 1996, *Orig. S.R.* $18.00
☆
1E $38   **2E $25**   **3E $20**
4E up $18
Have _____Want_____Price Paid _____

2820   **angel of freedom**   ☐

"As gentle as the sigh of an evening Angel..." – E.E. Smith

RETIRED, 1996

COMMENTS: Issued September 1994, *Orig. S.R.* $16.00

☆Both versions of this angel are to be retired this year so keep your eyes open for this piece. Version one is again the original version and the most sought after at this time. The second version is the GRS Edition.

Version 1: 1E $75   **2E $60**   **3E $50**
4E up $45
GRS Ed.: 1E $45   **2E $38**   **3E $32**
4E up $30

Have _____ Want _____ Price Paid _____

28201   **cosmos**   ☐

the gardening angel

"Heaven is under our feet as well as over our head." – Thoreau

COMMENTS: Issued Fall 1996, *Orig. S.R.* $19.00

☆

1E $55   **2E $40**   **3E $35**
4E $20   **5E up $19**

Have _____ Want _____ Price Paid _____

28202   **athena**   ☐

the wedding angel

"Come live with me and be my love..."
– Christopher Marlow

COMMENTS: Issued Fall 1996, *Orig. S.R.* $19.00

☆

1E $55   **2E $40**   **3E $25**
4E up $19

Have _____ Want _____ Price Paid _____

28203   **illumina**
angel of light
*"For a good angel will go with him, his
journey will be successful, and he will
come home safe and sound."*
– Apocrypha, Tobias 5:21
COMMENTS: Issued Fall 1996, *Orig. S.R.* $19.00
★
1E $55   **2E $35**   **3E $22**
4E up $19
Have _____ Want_____ Price Paid _____

28203-06 g.m.'s choice etheral
angel of light
LIMITED EDITION
*"Grace was in all her steps, heav'n in her
eyes..."* – John Milton
COMMENTS: Issued Fall 1996, *Orig. S.R.* $19.00
★Limited to 7,200 numbered pieces. On bottom of figurine the name is spelled *ethereal* with three e's.
#1-100 $150   **101-200 $140**   **201-1000 $135**
1001-7200 $125
Have _____ Want_____ Price Paid _____

28204   **serenity**
the mother's angel
*"God could not be everywhere and there-
fore made mothers."* – Jewish Proverb
COMMENTS: Issued Fall 1996, *Orig. S.R.* $19.00
★
1E $50   **2E $38**   **3E $22**
4E up $19
Have _____ Want_____ Price Paid _____

2821   **angel of love**   ☐

"No cord or cable can draw so forcibly, or bind so fast, as love can do with a single thread." – Robert Burton

RETIRED, 1996

COMMENTS: Issued September 1994, *Orig. S.R.* $16.00
☆Two versions have been produced of this figurine. The original figurine is version one, the second version is the GRS Edition (Resculpted). Eyes are extra large.

Version 1: 1E $85   **2E $60**   **3E $55**
4E up $50
GRS Ed.: 1E $55   **2E $50**   **3E $40**
4E up $16
Have _____ Want _____ Price Paid _____

2822   **angel of peace**   ☐

"Every visible thing in this world is the charge of an angel." – St. Augustine

TO BE RETIRED DECEMBER, 1997

COMMENTS: Issued September 1994, *Orig. S.R.* $16.00
☆

1E $70   **2E $40**   **3E $28**
4E up $16
GRS Ed.: 1E $50   **2E $30**   **3E $25**
4E up $16
Have _____ Want _____ Price Paid _____

2823   **oceana – ocean angel**   ☐

"There are other beaches to explore. There are more shells to find. This is only the beginning." – Anne Morrow Lindbergh

COMMENTS: Issued January 1995, *Orig. S.R.* $16.00
☆

1E $75   **2E $50**   **3E $22**
4E up $16
GRS Ed.: 1E $40   **2E $30**   **3E up $16**
Have _____ Want _____ Price Paid _____

2824   **florence** ☐
kitchen angel

*"Cooking is like love. It should be entered into
with abandon or not at all."* – H. VanHorne

RETIRED MARCH, 1995

COMMENTS: Issued January 1995, *Orig. S.R.* $19.00
☆There are three reported versions of this piece. The first
version has her hand on the bottom center of the bowl.
Version two has her hand placed on the right side of the
bowl. The third version is the GRS Edition figurine.

**Version 1: 1E $70   2E $60   3E $50
4E up $30
Version 2: 1E $70   2E $50   3E $45
4E up $30
GRS Ed.: 1E $55   2E $45   3E $38
4E up $30**

Have _____Want_____Price Paid _____

2825   **beatrice** ☐
birthday angel

*"Don't ever let yourself forget what its like
to be sixteen."* – Anon

RETIRED MARCH, 1995

COMMENTS: Issued January 1995, *Orig. S.R.* $19.00
☆Reports have been made of three different versions of this
figurine. Version one shows the candles on her head above
her hair. Version two's candles are even with her hair. The
third version is the GRS Edition.

**Version1: 1E $70   2E $60   3E $50
4E up $40
Version 2: 1E $65   2E $55   3E $45
4E up $40
GRS Ed.: 1E $55   2E $50   3E $40
4E up $40**

Have_____Want_____Price Paid _____

*At meetings of clubs, by an effort of will,
I always contrive to keep perfectly still,
For it takes but a word of annoyance or pity
And Wham! There I am on another committee.*

Alice F. Sturgis

2826   **minerva** □
the baseball angel
"Life is the game that must be played."
– E.A. Robinson
TO BE RETIRED DECEMBER, 1997
COMMENTS: Issued January 1995, *Orig. S.R.* $19.00
☆Two versions have been found on this figurine.
Version one has six buttons below her belt. Version
two has seven buttons below her belt.
Version 1: 1E $50   2E $40   3E $35
4E up $25
Version 2: 1E $40   2E $30   3E $25
4E up $20
Have _____ Want_____ Price Paid _____

2827   **lizzie** □
the shopping angel
"I never met a sale I didn't like."
– G.M. Lowenthal
RETIRED MARCH, 1995
COMMENTS: Issued January 1995, *Orig. S.R.* $19.00
☆Version one has her hand on the purse strap. This
version is probably the most sought after at this time.
Version two has her hand on the purse as well as the
strap. Version three is the GRS Edition.
Version 1: 1E $50   2E $40   3E $38
4E up $35
Version 2: 1E $45   2E $38   3E $35
4E up $35
GRS Ed.: 1E $45   2E $35   3E $30
4E up $30
Have _____ Want_____ Price Paid _____

2828   **seraphina with jacob & rachael** ☐
the choir angels
"Music is well said to be the speech of angels." – Thomas Carlyle
COMMENTS: Issued August 1995, *Orig. S.R.* $20.00
☆

1E $50	2E $38	3E $30
4E up $20		
GRS Ed.: 1E $30	2E $28	3E up $20

Have _____ Want _____ Price Paid _____

2829   **abigail** ☐
peaceable kingdom
"Blessed are the peacemakers; for they shall be called the children of God."
– Matthew 5:9
COMMENTS: Issued August 1995, *Orig. S.R.* $19.00
☆

1E $50	2E $38	3E $30
4E up $19		
GRS Ed.: 1E $30	2E $28	3E $20
4E up $19		

Have _____ Want _____ Price Paid _____

2830   **jingle moose** ☐
"Peace on Earth, Goodwill toward men..."
RETIRED DECEMBER, 1996
COMMENTS: Issued January 1995, *Orig. S.R.* $17.00
☆A favorite of many. There were two different versions of this piece.

Version 1: 1E $95	2E $90	3E $85
4E up $70		
GRS Ed.: 1E $70	2E $65	3E $55
4E up $50		

Have _____ Want _____ Price Paid _____

2831   **boowinkle – vonhinden moose** ☐

"They are given to all kinds of marvelous beliefs... and frequently see strange sights..." – Washington Irving

COMMENTS: Issued August 1995, *Orig. S.R.* $18.00

✫This figurine has two versions. Version 1 is the original version and the most sought after of the two. The second, less sought after version is the GRS Edition. Cute piece! Clever!

Version 1: 1E $65   **2E $45**   **3E $30**
4E up $25
GRS Ed.: 1E $40   **2E $22**   **3E up $18**
Have _____Want_____Price Paid _____

2833   **icabod mooselman** ☐

"No legacy is so rich as honesty."
– Shakespeare

COMMENTS: Issued August 1995, *Orig. S.R.* $18.00

✫mooselman – not mooseman. He is on my kitchen shelf with *prudence*! I used him in a Thanksgiving display.

1E $45   **2E $30**   **3E $20**
4E up $18
Have _____Want_____Price Paid _____

2834   **prudence mooselmaid** ☐
the pilgrim

"To everything there is a season, a time to every purpose under the sun."
– Ecclesiastes 3:1

COMMENTS: Issued August 1995, *Orig. S.R.* $18.00

✫I used her in a Thanksgiving display.

1E $45   **2E $30**   **3E $20**
4E up $18
Have _____Want_____Price Paid _____

2835   ernest hemmingmoose ☐
the hunter

"Nothing in life is so exhilarating as to be shot at without result," – Churchill

COMMENTS: Issued August 1995, *Orig. S.R.* $18.00

☆Had to have this one. The men in my family had a big laugh over him.

1E $55   **2E $35**   **3E up $18**

Have _____ Want_____ Price Paid _____

2836   beatrice ☐
the giftgiver

"They gave it to me – for an unbirthday present." – Lewis Carroll

COMMENTS: Issued August 1995, *Orig. S.R.* $18.00

☆

1E $50   **2E $30**   **3E up $18**

Have _____ Want_____ Price Paid _____

2837   egon ☐
the skier

"One can never consent to creep when one's impulse is to soar." – Helen Keller

COMMENTS: Issued Fall 1996, *Orig. S.R.* $18.00

☆

1E $50   **2E $25**   **3E up $18**

Have _____ Want_____ Price Paid _____

2840   **myrtle**   □
                  believe

"Where there is room in the heart there is always room in the house." – Thomas Moore

COMMENTS: Issued January 1995, *Orig. S.R.* $18.00

☆

1E $55   **2E $30**   **3E up $18**

Have _____Want_____Price Paid _____

2841   **peter**   □
                  the whopper

"Oh my fur and whiskers!... It's large as life and twice as natural." – Lewis Carroll

TO BE RETIRED DECEMBER, 1997

COMMENTS: Issued January 1995, *Orig. S.R.* $18.00

☆

Version 1: 1E $55   **2E $30**   **3E up $18**
GRS Ed.: 1E $30   **2E $22**   **3E $20**
4E up $18

Have _____Want_____Price Paid _____

2842   **jill**   □
                  language of love

"The little western flower upon which the bolt of Cupid fell." – *A Midsummer Night's Dream*

TO BE RETIRED DECEMBER, 1997

COMMENTS: Issued January 1995, *Orig. S.R.* $18.00

☆I wonder if his hearing is a little twisted? Popular!

1E $65   **2E $40**   **3E $20**
4E up $18

Have _____Want_____Price Paid _____

2843   **flora & amelia**
             the gardeners
             *"The goal of life is living in agreement with
             nature." – Zeno*
COMMENTS: Issued January 1996, *Orig. S.R.* $19.00
✮

1E $55   **2E $30**   **3E $20**
4E up $19
Have _____Want_____Price Paid _____

2844   **buster goes a 'courtin'**
             "Fortune favors the audacious." – Erasmus
COMMENTS: Issued January 1996, *Orig. S.R.* $19.00
✮Folkstone rabbits are popular. Great for Easter dec-
orations. Beware, they multiply!

1E $55   **2E $30**   **3E $20**
4E up $19
Have _____Want_____Price Paid _____

2845   **"too loose" – lapin**
             *"Imagination is more important than
             knowledge." – Albert Einstein*
COMMENTS: Issued January 1996, *Orig. S.R.* $19.00
✮

1E $55   **2E $25**   **3E $20**
4E up $19
Have _____Want_____Price Paid _____

2846 **flora, amelia & eloise** ☐
tea party
"Polly put the kettle on, we'll all have tea."
– Nursery Rhyme
COMMENTS: Issued January 1996, *Orig. S.R.* $19.00
✭

1E $48 **2E $30** **3E up $19**
Have _____Want_____Price Paid _____

2850 **rufus** ☐
hoe down
*"Live simply; expect little, give much...
Scatter sunshine."* – M.J. McLead
COMMENTS: Issued January 1995, *Orig. S.R.* $18.00
✭

1E $45 **2E $35** **3E up $25**
GRS Ed.: 1E $30 **2E $20** **3E up $18**
Have _____Want_____Price Paid _____

2851 **elmer** ☐
been farmin' long?
*"To plow and to sow, and to reap and to
mow, And to be a farmer's boy..."*
COMMENTS: Issued January 1995, *Orig. S.R.* $18.00
✭

1E $45 **2E $30** **3E up $18**
Have _____Want_____Price Paid _____

2852 **ida & bessie**
the gardeners
"A rich child often sits in a poor mother's lap." – Danish Proverb
COMMENTS: Issued January 1995, *Orig. S.R.* $18.00
★

1E $45	2E $30	3E up $25
GRS Ed.: 1E $30	2E $20	3E up $18

Have _____ Want _____ Price Paid _____

2853 **elmo "tex" beefcake**
on the range
"Trust iverybody...But cut th' ca-ards."
– Finley Peter
TO BE RETIRED DECEMBER, 1997
COMMENTS: Issued January 1996, *Orig. S.R.* $19.00
★

1E $45	2E $30	3E $20
4E up $19		

Have _____ Want _____ Price Paid _____

2854 **loretta moostein**
"cheatin' heart"
"Lookin' for love in all the wrong pastures..."
– E.E. Smith
COMMENTS: Issued January 1996, *Orig. S.R.* $19.00
★

1E $45	2E $30	3E $20
4E up $19		

Have _____ Want _____ Price Paid _____

2860 esmeralda ☐
the wonderful witch

"Around the world thoughts shall fly in the twinkling of an eye." – Att. to Mother Shipton

COMMENTS: Issued August 1995, *Orig. S.R.* $18.00
☆

1E $45 **2E $30** **3E $22**
4E up $18

Have _____Want_____Price Paid _____

2870 betty biscuit ☐

"Kissing don't last; cookery do!"
– G. Meredith

COMMENTS: Issued January 1996, *Orig. S.R.* $19.00
☆Poochstone – The original figurine's name was "betty cocker." This created a problem with the Betty Crocker company, a division of General Mills, so her name was changed to *betty biscuit.* It has been reported that "betty cocker" can be found up through the 8E. It is not clear if edition numbers went back to 1E with the change to *betty biscuit.* "betty cocker" would be the avid collectors' special find.

betty cocker
1E $75 **2E $50** **3E $45**
4E up $40
betty biscuit
insure at retail

Have _____Want_____Price Paid _____

2871 sparky mcplug ☐

"The will to do, the soul to dare."

COMMENTS: Issued January 1996, *Orig. S.R.* $19.00
☆Poochstone – Dalmatians are popular in any collectible!

1E $50 **2E $30** **3E $25**
4E up $19

Have _____Want_____Price Paid _____

2872   **alvin t. macbarker**   ☐
dog face
*"You can't build a reputation on what you
are going to do."*
TO BE RETIRED DECEMBER, 1997
COMMENTS: Issued January 1996, *Orig. S.R.* $19.00
☆Poochstone – Isn't he great?! A great piece for a
man's office or near his chair!

1E $75	2E $60	3E $50
4E up $40		

Have _____ Want_____ Price Paid _____

2873   **bernie**   ☐
igotwatiwanted st. bernard santa
*"Be great in Act as you have been in
Thought."* – Shakespeare
COMMENTS: Issued Fall 1996, *Orig. S.R.* $18.00
☆Poochstone – *bernie* is cute but could be a good
candidate, in my opinion, for retirement.

1E $45	2E $28	3E $25
4E up $18		

Have _____ Want_____ Price Paid _____

2899   **siegfried & egon - sign**   ☐
*"Promise, Large Promise, is the Soul of an
Advertisement."* – Samuel Johnson
COMMENTS: Issued August 1995, *Orig. S.R.* $19.00
☆Cute – A retirement candidate, in my opinion.

1E $55	2E $40	3E up $35
GRS 1E $30	2E $25	3E up $19

Have _____ Want_____ Price Paid _____

Santa & Friends Collection

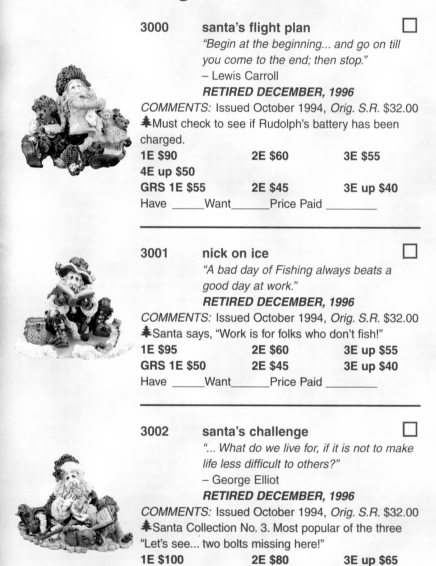

3000   **santa's flight plan**   ☐

"Begin at the beginning... and go on till you come to the end; then stop."
– Lewis Carroll
RETIRED DECEMBER, 1996

COMMENTS: Issued October 1994, *Orig. S.R.* $32.00
🌲Must check to see if Rudolph's battery has been charged.

1E $90	**2E $60**	**3E $55**
4E up $50		
GRS 1E $55	**2E $45**	**3E up $40**

Have _____Want_____Price Paid _____

3001   **nick on ice**   ☐

"A bad day of Fishing always beats a good day at work."
RETIRED DECEMBER, 1996

COMMENTS: Issued October 1994, *Orig. S.R.* $32.00
🌲Santa says, "Work is for folks who don't fish!"

1E $95	**2E $60**	**3E up $55**
GRS 1E $50	**2E $45**	**3E up $40**

Have _____Want_____Price Paid _____

3002   **santa's challenge**   ☐

"... What do we live for, if it is not to make life less difficult to others?"
– George Elliot
RETIRED DECEMBER, 1996

COMMENTS: Issued October 1994, *Orig. S.R.* $32.00
🌲Santa Collection No. 3. Most popular of the three "Let's see... two bolts missing here!"

1E $100	**2E $80**	**3E up $65**
GRS 1E $55	**2E $50**	**3E up $50**

Have _____Want_____Price Paid _____

3003   santa... December 26 □
"At Christmas play and make good cheer,
For Christmas comes but once a year."
– T. Tusser
"Thank goodness!" – Santa
RETIRED DECEMBER, 1996
COMMENTS: Issued December 1995, *Orig. S.R.* $32.00
🌲Santa Collection No. 4

1E $95	2E $80	3E up $55
GRS 1E $45	2E up $40	

Have _____Want_____Price Paid _____

3004   santa's hobby... the bearmaker □
"To wake the soul by tender strokes of art,
To raise the genius, and to mend the
heart..." – Alexander Pope
GCC EXCLUSIVE
COMMENTS: Issued November 1996, *Orig. S.R.* $35.00
🌲

GCC Ed. 1E $50	2E up $35

Have _____Want_____Price Paid _____

Faerie Collection

The Faerie Collection is a new line of Folkstones that represents our friends
and helpers. This collection is limited to 4,800 pieces in each edition.

3600   fixit □
santa's faerie
"Imagination is more important than
knowledge." – Albert Einstein
COMMENTS: Issued Fall 1996, *Orig. S.R.* $18.00
⭐This piece is "too young" for much secondary
market trading to be found. Faeries haven't been a
sought after collectible in other lines.

1E $30	2E $25	3E up $18

Have _____Want_____Price Paid _____

DOLLSTONES™

Each Dollstone figurine (not musical) is marked on the base with the series name, the number it is in that series and the hand-written edition numeral. Dollstones are produced in editions of 4,800 pieces.

2720 ♪ **megan with elliot...**
christmas carol
LIMITED EDITION

COMMENTS: Issued Fall 1996, *Orig. S.R.* $39.00
💬 Musical waterball limited to 12 months production.
Plays: *Amazing Grace.*

1E $70	2E $45	3E $42
4E up $39		

Have _____ Want _____ Price Paid _____

3500 **jennifer with priscilla...**
the doll in the attic
"A sweet child is the sweetest thing in
nature." – Charles Lamb

COMMENTS: Issued February 1996, *Orig. S.R.* $20.50
💬 **Home Again Series, No. 1.** It has been reported this Dollstone was found with "Premier Edition" on the base. This figurine never appeared on QVC.

Prem. Ed. $140	1E $65	2E $40
3E $28	4E up $20.50	

Have _____ Want _____ Price Paid _____

3501 **patricia with molly...**
attic treasures
"Little Friends may prove
great Friends." – Aesop

COMMENTS: Issued February 1996, *Orig. S.R.* $14.00
💬 **Home Again Series, No. 2.** This Dollstone never appeared on QVC but reports of "Premier Edition" have been found on this piece.

Prem. Ed. $135	1E $65	2E $40
3E $25	4E up $14	

Have _____ Want _____ Price Paid _____

$\mathcal{R}$eminder...

According to Boyds, Dollstone *jennifer with priscilla* (#3500) and *patricia with molly* (#3501) are understamped "Premier Edition" but were never released on QVC. (See page 68.)

3502   **victoria with samantha...**   ☐
          victorian ladies

"What is a Friend? A single soul dwelling in two bodies." – Aristotle

COMMENTS: Issued August 1995, *Orig. S.R.* $20.00
✌ Victorian Series, No. 1. One of the first four to debut on QVC.

Prem. Ed. $150	1E $75	2E $60
3E $50	4E up $20	

Have _____Want_____Price Paid _____

3503   **betsy with edmund...**   ☐
          the patriots

"I, for one, know of no sweeter sight for a man's eyes than his own country."
– Homer

COMMENTS: Issued August 1995, *Orig. S.R.* $20.00
✌ Home Again Series, No. 3. One of the first four to debut on QVC.

Prem. Ed. $140	1E $60	2E $40
3E $25	4E up $20	

Have _____Want_____Price Paid _____

BC3503-1 betsy with edmund...   ☐
          the patriots

"I, for one, know of no sweeter sight for a man's eyes than his own country."
– Homer

COMMENTS: Issued February 1996, *Orig. S.R.* $22.95
✌ Home Again Series, No. 3. Original suggested retail price is U.S. funds. Add duty, shipping and handling fees.

1E $70	2E $45	3E $30
4E up $22.95		

Have _____Want_____Price Paid _____

Did You Know?

A sneak preview of four figurines from Boyds was introduced on QVC in August, 1995. Those Dollstones introduced were: *victoria with samantha* (#3502), *betsy with edmund* (#3503), *megan with elliot and annie* (#3504) and *katherine with amanda and edmund* (#3505). There were approximately 3,600 of each figurine. They were marked "Premier Edition," and were sold out immediately! Many did not see this QVC show and these first Dollstones took us all by a whirl! Overnight, the secondary market increased on these by about 400%.

3504   **megan with elliot & annie...** ☐
christmas carol
"I will honor Christmas in my heart and try to keep it all the year."
– A Christmas Carol
COMMENTS: Issued August 1995, *Orig. S.R.* $20.00
❣️ One of the first four to debut on QVC.

Prem. Ed. $350	1E $80	2E $40
3E $30	4E up $20	

Have _____ Want _____ Price Paid _____

3505   **katherine with amanda & edmund...** ☐
kind hearts
"For I will believe... and trust thee, gentle Kate." – Shakespeare
COMMENTS: Issued August 1995, *Orig. S.R.* $20.00
❣️ **I Wannabe Series, No. 1.** One of the first four to debut on QVC.

Prem. Ed. $150	1E $75	2E $40
3E $30	4E up $20	

Have _____ Want _____ Price Paid _____

"Our prayer of thanks for the laughter of children who tumble bare-footed and bare-headed in the summer grass." - Carl Sandburg

3506   **ashley with christie...** ☐
dress up

*"One of the most beautiful qualities of true
friendship is to understand and to be
understood."* – Seneca

COMMENTS: Issued January 1996, *Orig. S.R.* $20.50
❣I **Wannabe Series, No. 2.** Part of the second set to
debut on QVC.

Prem. Ed. $75	1E $65	2E $30
3E $25	4E up $20.50	

Have _____Want_____Price Paid _____

Did You Know?

GCC stands for Gift Creations Concepts. GCC is a group of dealers who pay
a fee to be members of this association. Through GCC's large buying power,
member dealers are able to offer exclusive items through their stores. GCC
stores provide gift catalogs to their customers, offering these gift and often
limited collectibles exclusively. Two offerings of GCC exclusive figurines are
courtney with phoebe (#3512-01) and *christy with nicole* (#3516).

3507   **sarah & heather with elliot,** ☐
dolly & amelia...
tea for four

LIMITED EDITION

*" We cannot tell the precise moment when
friendship is formed. As in filling a vessel
drop by drop, there is at las a drop which
makes it run over; so in a series of kindness there is at least one which makes
the heart run over."*

COMMENTS: Issued January 1996, *Orig. S.R.* $46.00
❣ **Limited Edition, No. 1.** A large piece. Part of the
second set to debut on QVC. Not marked Limited
Edition on the base. Limited to production during
1996. Premier Edition was limited to 2,400 pieces.
Later editions were limited to 3,600 pieces.

Prem. Ed. $ 145	1E $110	2E $75
3E $55	4E up $50	

Have _____Want_____Price Paid _____

3508   **emily with kathleen and otis...**   ☐
the future

"The most precious possession that ever comes to a man in this world is a woman's heart." – Holland

COMMENTS: Issued January 1996, *Orig. S.R.* $30.00
👣 **I Wannabe Series, No. 3.** According to Boyds, this has been the most popular piece in the Dollstone™ series, to date. A gorgeous piece for sure! Part of the second set to debut on QVC.

Prem. Ed. $95	**1E $80**	**2E $40**
3E $35	**4E up $30**	

Have _____ Want _____ Price Paid _____

3509   **rebecca with elliot...**   ☐
birthday!

"The birthday of my life has come. my love has come to me." – Rossetti

COMMENTS: Issued January 1996, *Orig. S.R.* $20.50
👣 **Celebration Series, No. 1.** Part of the second set to debut on QVC. This QVC premier edition was to be limited to 4,800 pieces but editions over 5,000 were discovered. Not really sought after. Could be retired, in my opinion.

Prem. Ed. $70	**1E $60**	**2E $30**
3E $25	**4E up $20.50**	

Have _____ Want _____ Price Paid _____

3510   **jean with elliot & debbie...**   ☐
the bakers

"Remember this – that very little is needed to make a happy life." – Marcus Aurelius

COMMENTS: Issued August 1996, *Orig. S.R.* $20.00
👣 **Home Again Series, No 4.** Part of the third set to debut on QVC. We have heard of a store exclusive of this piece to debut late 1996 or early 1997. Read the *Weekly Collectors' Gazette™* to keep informed.

Prem. Ed. $60	**1E $50**	**2E $30**
3E $22	**4E up $20**	

Have _____ Want _____ Price Paid _____

3511   **michelle with daisy...** ☐
       reading is fun
       "To be able to be caught up into the world
       of thought – that is being educated."
       – Edith Hamilton

Comments: Issued August 1996, *Orig. S.R.* $18.00
💬❗ **I Wannabe Series, No 4.** Part of the third set to debut on QVC.

Prem. Ed. $65	1E $40	2E $25
3E $20	4E up $18	

Have _____Want_____Price Paid _____

3512   **courtney with phoebe...** ☐
       over the river and through the woods
       "I have led her home, my love, my only
       friend. There is none like her, none."
       – Alfred, Lord Tennyson

COMMENTS: Issued August 1996, *Orig. S.R.* $25.00
💬 **Home Again Series, No. 5.** Very nice piece!

1E $65	2E $35	3E $30
4E up $25		

Have _____Want_____Price Paid _____

Did You Know?

Of the three GCC Dollstone early releases only one, *courtney with phoebe* (#3512-01), has a color difference from its 1E release. All three GCC early releases, *courtney with phoebe* (#3512-01), *karen with wilson and eloise* (#3515) and *christy with nicole* (#3516), will have a special understamp. (See page VI.)

3512-01   **courtney with phoebe...** ☐
       over the river and through the woods
       "I have led her home, my love, my only
       friend. There is none like her, none."
       – Alfred, Lord Tennyson
       GCC EXCLUSIVE (GCC Dealers)

COMMENTS: Issued August 1996, *Orig. S.R.* $27.50
💬 **Home Again Series, No. 5.** Early release with special understamp and color difference. Look above to compare the different scarf and sweater colors.

GCC Ed. 1E $70	2E $40	3E $38
4E up $35		

Have _____Want_____Price Paid _____

3514 **candice with matthew...** ☐
gathering apples
"Come, ye thankful people, come, raise the
song of harvest home..." – Henry Alford
COMMENTS: Issued August 1996, *Orig. S.R.* $19.00
Home Again Series, No 6. Part of the third set to
debut on QVC.

Prem. Ed. $50   **1E $40**   **2E $30**
3E $28   **4E up $25**
Have _____Want_____Price Paid _____

3515 **karen with wilson & eloise...** ☐
mother's present
"Who ran to help me when I fell, and
would some pretty story tell, or kiss the
place to make it well? My Mother!"
– Jane Taylor
COMMENTS: Issued August 1996, *Orig. S.R.* $26.00
Celebration Series, No 3. The only difference
between the retailers' version and the GCC edition is
the understamp.

1E $50   **2E $35**   **3E up $26**
GCC Ed. 1E $50   **2E $35**   **3E up $26**
Have _____Want_____Price Paid _____

"Children are the true connoisseurs.
What's precious to them has no price - only value." - Bel Kaufman

3516 **christy with nicole...** ☐
skaters
"It is one of the most beautiful compensations
of life that no one can sincerely try to help
another, without helping onesself.
– John P. Webster
GCC EXCLUSIVE
COMMENTS: Issued November 1996, *Orig. S.R.* $26.00
Home Again Series, No 7. GCC early release has
a special understamp. (Predicted prices.)

GCC Ed. 1E $65   **2E $50**   **3E $45**
4E up $30
Have _____Want_____Price Paid _____

3517   **mallory with patsy & jb...** ☐
halloween

*"Backward, turn backward, O Time in thy
flight; make me a child again, just for
tonight."* – Elizabeth Akers Allen

COMMENTS: Issued August 1996, *Orig. S.R.* $27.00
Celebration Series, No 4. Of the four Dollstones
to premier on the QVC Collectors' Day Show on
August 3, 1996, *mallory* was the first to sell out. At
that time G.M. Lowenthal stated that this figurine was
exclusive to QVC (it may or may not be released to
dealers in the future) and not as many of this figurine
were produced in the Premier Edition as compared to
the other three Dollstones shown. Price rose to $175
early; may be found for less.
Prem. Ed. $135-175
Have _____ Want _____ Price Paid _____

3599   **anne...** ☐
the masterpiece

*"Whatever you do, or dream you can do.
begin it. Boldness has genius, power and
magic in it. –* Geothe

COMMENTS: Issued August 1996, *Orig. S.R.* $24.00
Found with an errored box marked "anna."

1E $60	2E $30	3E up $24

Have _____ Want _____ Price Paid _____

*Sydney Hocker
is proud to show
you some of
her favorite
Dollstones.
What little girl
wouldn't love to
have a Dollstone
Collection?*

New Pieces for 1997

Bearstones
#227701-07	edmund... the graduate - carpe diem	$17.00
#227701-10	bailey... the graduate - carpe diem	$17.00
#227702	neville... compubear	$16.50
#227703	humboldt... the simple bear	$12.00
#227704	bailey... poor ol' bear	$15.00
#227705	louella & hedda... the secret	$19.00
#227706	buzz... the flash	$18.00

Bearstone – 1997 Limited Edition
#227801	the flying lesson... this end up	$61.00

Bearstone Holiday Pageant
#2408	essex... as the donkey	$15.00
#2409	winkie & dink... as the lambs	$12.00
#2410	bruce... as the shepherd	$15.00
#2411	ariel & clarence... as the angel pair (set of two)	$15.00

Waterglobes
#270550	homer on the plate	$35.00

Bearstone Votives
#27750	daphne... in the cabbage patch	$26.00
#27751	ms. bruin & bailey... tea time	$26.00

Shoe Box Bears
#3203	madison... "the goil" grizberg	$10.50

Folkstones
#28240	mercy... angel of nurses	$19.00
#28241	ms. patience... angel of teachers	$19.00
#2838	ziggy... the duffer	$19.00
#2847	prudence... daffodils	$19.00
#2874	sgt. rex & matt... the runaway	$19.50

Folkstones 1997 Limited Edition
#28205	constance & felicity... best friend angels	$37.00

Wee Folkstone
#36100	angelina "smidge" angellove... angel of true love	$16.00
#36101	infinite faerielove... the wedding faerie	$16.00
#36102	dentinate "faeriefloss"... the tooth faerie	$16.00
#36300	"electra" angelbyte... angel in computer training	$18.00
#36301	estudious "cram" faeriebaum... the study faerie	$18.00
#36302	immaculata faerieburg... the cleaning faerie	$18.00
#65430	mini woodland log	$ 5.50

Yesterdays' Child
#3519	natalie with joy... sunday school	$23.00
#3520	julia with emmy lou & daphne... garden friends	$20.00
#3521	wendy with bronte, keats, tennyson, & poe... wash day	$23.00
#3522	laura with jane... first day of school	$23.00
#3523	whitney with wilson... tea party	$20.00

Dollstones 1997 Limited Edition
#3518	the amazing bailey... magic show at 4"	$56.00

Dollstones Votives
#27950	whitney with wilson... tea and candle light	$26.00

A Collector's Story

Pat Santos with the "Head Bean Hisself"

In the fall of 1994, I had just come from picking apples in a local orchard. My neighbor, Perk, came over for coffee with a resin figurine she had just bought at a shop. She thought I might like it. It happened to be *bailey in the orchard* and she was right, I loved it immediately with its antique style, a patch here, a tear there, etc. It was from The Boyds Collection™ and was called Bearstones™. I had to have one! Perk went to the shop again and bought me one. She said there were other figurines that I might like. The next week Perk and I went there. I had no idea what I was in for – I bought others. I was HOOKED!! I loved them all, with their different styles and verses (quotes) they were so unique. I found myself writing to The Boyds Collection, Ltd., to find out more about them. (How many were produced, where to find them, if they had a catalog, etc.)

Later, my sister-in-law bought me a Bearstone™ I didn't have. It was *grenville... the graduate*. I looked on the bottom and it was a "1st Edition." WOW!! Well, I decided I was going to try to find all 1Es.

What a challenge! That's when I realized that I had become a "Collector." These figurines are so well done and so reasonably priced, it was easy to get started. Now I'm Hooked!

I realize, as I keep looking at my figurines, that they remind me of people in my life. For example, *clara the nurse* – my neighbor Perk; *victoria the lady* – my cousin and best friend, Dot; *elliot the hero* – my daughter, Christine (she works for the Fire Dept. as a secretary). I could go on and on.

Since I started collecting, Boyds has expanded from Bearstones™ to Folkstones™, Sánta & Friends™, Poochstones™, Dollstones™, Shoe Box Bears™ and Faeries™. It's so much fun when you mention the name Boyds to someone who collects something. What a great way to make new friends. Finally, after two years of asking about a club, Boyds has introduced one! I'm waiting for my Membership Kit to the Official Original F.o.B. in the Loyal Order of Friends of Boyds!! It should come soon..

Your Friend,

Pat Santos

FRIENDS

Sharing The Fun Of Collecting

Sue Hall

Recently a friend of mine got me started collecting the Dollstones. My first piece was the limited edition *tea for four*. I was so impressed with all the detail in each figurine. After that I couldn't resist the Bearstones and Folkstones. I also have a few plush bears and hares.

Ione Wood

I think Boyds bears are a hidden treasure. I discovered them in early '95 and I was hooked, after purchasing *to have and to hold*. The detail and the unique craftmanship is marvelous. I've expanded my collection to include Dollstones. My favorite piece is *tea for four* because I received it from a close friend (Susan Hall). They are a joy to collect with friends.

RETIRED BEARSTONES

BEARSTONES

Indexed by Name

Indexed by Subject

Canadian Pieces

San Francisco Music Boxes
Indexed by Name

RETIRED FOLKSTONES

FOLKSTONES

Indexed by Name

Indexed by Subject

DOLLSTONES

Indexed by Name

Unofficial Series List

Canadian Pieces

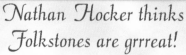

*Nathan Hocker thinks
Folkstones are grrreat!*

Notes

This Guide Belongs To:

Name_____

Address_____

Phone_____

If you find this lost guide...
please return to Desperate Collector above.